A Pictorial History
of Gold Mining
in the
Blue Mountains of
Eastern Oregon

by

Howard Brooks

Third Printing - September 2013

Foreword

Howard Brooks, retired geologist, was employed by Oregon Department of Geology and Mineral Industries (DOGAMI) 1956-91. This book represents Brooks' ongoing interest and research into the mining areas of Northeastern Oregon. His descriptions of the various mining areas are not intended to be all inclusive. Many prospect holes and numerous small mines dotted most of the mining areas discussed in this book, but even naming them all would be an exhaustive procedure. For example, two of the areas which he covers contain nearly 100 named mines and prospects, as identified in early maps which Brooks helped to create: Bourne Quadrangle (DOGAMI #GMS 19, 1982) lists 61 named mines: Aldora, Cracker Creek dredge placer, Ellis Mine, McCully Fork dredge placer, Downie placer, Porcupine group, Midway-Banshee, Bunker Hill, Morning Star, Cracker-Klondike, Analulu, Mayfloer-Grayrock, Amazon, Mountain Belle, Free Coinage-Brooklyn, Silver Dick, Big Pine Group, Golden Gate, Telegraph, Golconda, Climax, S. Minneapolis, Old Middleman, Columbia, Taber Fraction, Victor, Cracker-Oregon, Eureka and Excelsior, Cracker-Summit, Dutchman, Rawlson, Soudan, King Pin, North Pole, Lakeview Spring, Ninestrike, Sampson and Risk, Buckeye, South Pole, Jim Blaine Platt Group, Chloride, Black Crow, Midas, Western Union, Kelly, MountainView, Esmerelda, Boston, Argonaut, Molly Gibson, Gold Coin Consolidated; Elkhorn Peak Quadrangle (DOGAMI #GMS-41, 1987): Cumberland, General Sherman, Derning Group, Pearl, ElkhornBonanza, Excuse, Cub, Chloride, Midnight, Highland-Maxwell Group, Defender, Shamrock, Brooklyn, Highland Vein, Highland-Maxwell Group, Bottom, Bottom Dollar, Maxwell, Mountain Belle Vein, Mountain View, Miners Hope, Denny Group, Missouri Girl, Captain Jack, Bonanza Queen, Blue Ledge, Baisley Elkhorn, Accident, Tired Miner, Dolcoatte, Delaware, Randall and McCord, LeRoi, Bear Hole, Tamarack Group, Quarry Overiview, Marble Creek Quarry, Golden Eagle, Lake Creek prospect, Iron Mask, Baboon Creek Quarry, S. Louis, Paymaster, Deer Creek placers, Old Abe. Not listed are the approximately 30 or so identified mining sites for which the names have been lost. Persons interested in such complete lists and the locations of each mine should consult DOGAMI maps and documents.

Howard Brooks

The collection of historic photos are from many sources, including Baker County Public Library, Baker City; Oregon Trail Regional Museum, Baker City; Grant County Oregon Museum, Canyon City; Oregon Department of Geology and Mineral Industries, Baker City; and from a number of individuals who have an interest in mining, and/or are collectors of historic photos. Also included are contemporary photos of some mining areas, taken by Howard Brooks and others, with other assistance from Brooks Hawley, Sumpter historian; Doris King, whose father was a miner in Bourne, Mormon Basin, and Greenhorn; Terry Drever-Gee, Bonnanza Mining Co.; Walter Forsea, Richland rancher; Chary Mires, Oregon Trail Regional Museum; Howard Brooks' sons, James, Daniel, Michael; Jan Durflinger of DOGAMI, Baker City; and the staff of Grant County Museum, Canyon City; and many old friends who like to talk mining. Cover: "Elkhorns as seen from Sumpter Valley" by Gary Dielman.

Howard Brooks says, "This book is a labor of love. There's always more I could include, but it's time to call it good...and maybe start on volume two," he adds with a wry grin.

--Eloise Dielman, editor

Published by Baker County Historical Society, 2007.
P.O. Box 83
Baker City, OR 97814

Contents

4

Above: Unnamed Eastern Oregon mine. Photo from McCord Collection, Baker County Public Library.

Pictorial History of Gold Mining in Northeastern Oregon

Text by Howard Brooks, retired geologist,
employed by Oregon Department of Geology and Mineral Industries 1956-91.

Historic photos are from many sources, including Baker County Public Library, Baker City;
Oregon Trail Regional Museum, Baker City; Grant County Oregon Museum, Canyon City;
Oregon Department of Geology and Mineral Industries (DOGAMI), Baker City;
and from a number of individuals including Doris King, and Flint Stearns.

Index maps are reprinted from Brooks and Ramp, 1968.

Howard would like to give special thanks to Eloise Dielman. Without her technical and editorial help
this book would not have been published.

Howard dedicates this book to his family.

Preface

The gold rush era of the latter half of the 1800s is among the most fascinating chapters in western American history. More than a million people became actively involved and hundreds of millions of dollars worth of gold was produced in those exciting times. Most importantly, the gold rushes greatly hastened the settlement of the western United States.

The rushes began with the discovery of gold at Sutter's Mill in California in 1848 and spread to localities in southwest Oregon in 1852; northeastern Washington, British Columbia and Colorado in the late 1850s; Nevada's great Comstock Lode in 1859; eastern Oregon, western Idaho, and western Montana in the early 1860s; and Alaska and the Yukon in 1896. The rushes for gold in the western United States coincided with the rush to obtain farm and ranch land under the Donation Land Claims Act of 1850 and the Homestead Act of 1862.

When Oregon became a state in 1859, there were no permanent white settlers in the area of northeastern Oregon and adjacent western Idaho shown on the map (p. 8). Tens of thousands of Oregon trail emigrants had already passed through the Boise River, Powder River, and Grande Ronde River Valleys since 1843. Probably many pioneers noted the potential value of the land therein for agricultural pursuits but there were no markets for agricultural products, no sources of the supplies, equipment, livestock, and seed for planting, or any of the things needed for farm and ranch maintenance. There was also little protection from marauding Indians, so the immigrants traveled on to the Willamette Valley.

That all changed rather quickly in the early 1860s when gold was discovered in several places and thousands of people flocked to the region in search of their Eldorado. Thousands came to find and mine the gold and thus created an instant market for a vast amount of food and other supplies and services. Thousands more came to provide those needs. Many took up land claims in the valleys and began raising crops and livestock for food. Others started sawmills and timber companies to provide lumber for building and wood for heating and food preparation. Others built roads to the mining camps and farm towns. Transportation companies were formed to haul freight and passengers. Local governments, churches and schools were soon established. Initially much of this activity was paid for by money from the gold mines. Gold production remained a major part of the region's economy for several decades until the farm, ranch, and timber industries could stand on their own.

Mining camps sprang up almost over night wherever gold was found. Most were established in the mountainous areas while many small farm settlements grew in the valleys. Among the better known early day mining camps were Orofino, Pierce, Elk City, Florence, Warren, and Idaho City in Idaho; and Auburn, Canyon City, Granite, Sumpter, Clarksville, and Malheur City in Oregon. By 1863 these and many smaller camps were collectively producing millions of dollars in gold annually.

The populations of some of the gold camps grew explosively to thousands, and then dwindled almost as quickly to hundreds as late comers learned that the good claims were already taken and the more restless inhabitants were enticed away by reports of new and richer discoveries elsewhere. Most of the early gold discoveries were made by groups of men led by experienced California miners who came looking for new diggings when the bonanza placers of the California gold rush that started in 1848 were nearing exhaustion and many miners found themselves without jobs.

Gold mining in the Blue Mountains of northeastern Oregon began on October 23, 1861, with the discovery of gold in a gulch, later named Griffin Gulch, near present-day Baker City. The discovery was made by part of a group of men who were searching for the legendary Blue Bucket Mine. According to that legend, in 1845, a wagon train led by Stephen Meek bound for the Willamette Valley via an unproven shortcut, became lost for a while somewhere in Eastern Oregon. Children in the party, while playing in a creek, found yellow pebbles that they placed in a blue bucket that was forgotten and left at the site when the train moved on. A few specimens of the pebbles were carried on to Portland in a toolbox and later identified as gold.

Despite many searches, the source of the yellow pebbles has never been positively identified although some (see Miles F. Potter, *Oregon's Golden Years,* 1982) subscribe to the idea that the site was on Canyon Creek near present-day Canyon City, which later proved to be one of the most productive placer gold camps in northeastern Oregon.

In the fall of 1861, a party of 50 men, including several from the California gold fields on their way to new gold discoveries in Idaho, assembled in Portland under the leadership of a man named Adams and traveled on horseback to eastern Oregon searching for the site that by then was known as the "Lost Blue Bucket Mine." After finally realizing that Adams had no idea of the Blue Bucket Mine's location, the men split up. Some went on east to the new Idaho gold camps, some headed back to Portland, the remainder continued searching and on October 23, 1861, found gold in the gulch now known as Griffin Gulch near present Baker City.

To avoid spending the soon-to-come winter in the wilderness, most of the group returned to Portland, but Henry Griffin and three companions (David Littlefield, G.W. Schriver, & William Stafford) [Some say a fifth man stayed], all from California gold fields, made a round trip to Walla Walla for supplies. They then built a cabin and spent the winter investigating their discovery and getting ready to mine in the spring. In late winter a couple of the men made a second trip to Walla Walla and paid for merchandise purchased at that time with Griffin Gulch gold. Some of that gold was taken to Portland where it was prominently displayed, thus triggering a rush of prospectors to northeastern Oregon. Diary entries in the book *Powerful Rocky* indicate that prospectors were mining placer gold deposits on Burnt River as early as 1854.

In early spring, 1862, gold was found in Blue Canyon about four miles south of Griffin Gulch. The town of Auburn, the first town in the Blue Mountains, was established there. By late fall Auburn had a mile long main street, 500 rough lumber buildings and tents, and for a short time had a population of about 5,000, making it larger than Portland's 1860 population of nearly 3000 people. Local government, a school, churches, small businesses and many saloons had been started.

Legendary Blue Bucket Mine story as told by Isaac Hiatt, an 1860s miner who lived in Baker County until the 1890's. A wagon train led by Stephen Meek bound for the Willamette Valley via an unproven shortcut, became lost for a while somewhere in Eastern Oregon. Children in the party, while playing in a creek, found yellow pebbles that they placed in a blue bucket that was forgotten and left at the site when the train moved on. A few specimens of the pebbles were carried on to Portland in a toolbox and later identified as gold.

Also in early 1862, gold was discovered in Canyon Creek, about 80 miles to the west of Auburn. The camp started there was first called Whiskey Gulch then Canyon City and later in the year, like Auburn, had a population said to be about 5,000.

By the end of 1863, most of the other placer mining districts known today in northeastern Oregon had been discovered and mining camps established including Canyon City, Auburn, Quartzburg, Granite, Clarksville, and Mormon Basin. [For further descriptions of these and other

1860s Pacific Northwest Supply Routes and Centers

places see the respective chapters under "Gold Mining Districts and Towns."]

Some of the gold field stampeders were Willamette Valley pioneers who backtracked along the Oregon Trail to the new gold diggings. Some came part way by steamboat up the Columbia and Snake Rivers. Many others came overland from California and states to the east, including Mormon settlers from Utah. Some Oregon Trail immigrants on their way west turned off the trail near Flagstaff Hill to see what the ruckus at Auburn was all about and stayed to take part in the development of this new land.

By the end of 1863, most of the placer mining districts known today in northeastern Oregon had been discovered and mining camps established including Canyon City, Auburn, Quartzburg, Granite, Clarksville,and Mormon Basin.

Above: Early Canyon City, Grant County.

The Gold Producing Belt

The gold producing belt is about 120 miles long and 40 miles wide, extending from the John Day area east to the Snake River. The mines have produced 3,500,000 ounces of gold (about 150 tons) and an equal amount of silver. Two mines, both in Baker county, produced significant amounts of copper as well as gold and silver, the Iron Dyke at Homestead and the Mother Lode near Keating. Many gold mines produced small amounts of copper, lead and zinc as minor by-products.

About half of the gold and silver production was from surface placers and half from underground lode mines. Although lode mines began operating as early as 1864, most of the gold production between 1862 and the mid-1880s was from placer deposits because they were the most easily found and could be worked largely by hand. Lode mining required heavy, expensive equipment, much of it made of iron and steel, that had to be hauled overland, usually from The Dalles or Umatilla by wagon or pack train. Digging tunnels and shafts deep into the ground following gold bearing veins was dangerous as well as expensive work.

Production History

Northeastern Oregon gold mines have produced about 3,500,000 ounces of gold and an equal amount of silver. Production had many ups and downs. The 3,500,000 ounces produced in northeastern Oregon is about 60 percent of all the gold and silver produced in the state of Oregon. Because parts of many placers found in the earliest days of mining were very rich and many miners and would be miners were available to work them, the first few years after discovery very likely marked the high point of production. Unfortunately, no one kept consistent records of how much gold was actually produced by any mine or district during those early years.

However, so great was the influx of miners in the early days of mining that by the 1870s overall placer production had dwindled appreciably.

Brooks and Ramp say, "Sketchy records indicate that many of the early diggings were rich, but there are no reliable statistics to show the total amount of gold produced in eastern Oregon during the period of 1861-1880" (1968, p. 43). Production probably was at its peak during 1863-1866, then began to decline gradually as the richest placers were worked out. Raymond (1870) estimated that production from the placers of Canyon Creek averaged about $22,000 per week during the mining season of 1865. In 1869, output averaged about $8,000 per week from April to October and perhaps $20,000 per month the rest of the year. For the year 1870, Raymond (1872) estimated the total shipments of gold from eastern Oregon exclusive of Canyon City and other districts west of the Blue Ranges at $600,000. W. H. Packwood stated that "the yearly gold output of Baker and Union Counties cannot have been less than from one to one and one-half million dollars from 1863 to 1870. The gold has been, we may say, the sole product of labor. The number of miners has been from one to three thousand averaging for several years about fifteen hundred" (in Raymond, 1872, p. 184) . By 1914, according to Pardee and Hewett , "the placer mines of the Sumpter quadrangle had produced a minimum of $5,231,000 in gold and silver" (1914, pp. 10-11). They suggested the total output exceeded that figure.

Brooks and Ramp further stated, "Estimates of production are available for few placers outside the Sumpter quadrangle." In his account on the Canyon area , Lindgren said "It is scarcely probable that the total production of that area, much exceeds $15,000,000" (1901, pp. 712-720). Others claim as much as $26,000,000 was produced. Swartley credits the placers of Elk Creek near Susanville with total output of approximately $600,000 (1914, p. 169) and suggests the same figure for the Dixie Creek placers (p. 198). Swartley also states that production from the Rye Valley placers amounted to more than $1,000,000 (p. 228). The placers near Sanger reportedly produced about $500,000 in gold by the year 1901 (Lindgren, 1901, p .738).

Lode mining developed rapidly following extension of the railroad to Baker City in 1884. Completion of the Sumpter Valley Railroad to Sumpter in 1896 facilitated a lode mining boom in that area that lasted until about 1910. Sumpter's population grew rapidly to 3,000 or more. Many of the most productive mines of the region were developed during this period. There was also considerable speculation. Much money was unwisely invested in worthless prospects. Gold production reached another high during the late 1930s and early 1940s following the increase of the price of gold from $20.67 to $35.00 per troy ounce in 1934. This increase was promoted by President Roosevelt as a way to create employment and increase money supplies during the great depression of the 1930s.

Early in World War II, gold mining was curtailed by order of the War Production Board. The board said that the men and materials affected could be better used elsewhere in the war effort. Few mines were reactivated after the war mainly because materials and labor costs had risen greatly while the price of gold remained fixed at $35.00 for more than 40 years after the war ended. By the time gold prices were allowed to rise, the old lode mines were in such deteriorated condition that rehabilitation would have been prohibitively expensive. Also the public demand for gold has for many years been supplied by large open pit mines. The operating expenses per ounce of gold produced from an open pit mine are much less than the expenses of operating the small underground mines known in northeastern Oregon would be.

Northeastern Oregon gold production since World War II has come largely from placer deposits. The Sumpter Valley Dredge was reactivated in 1946 and operated steadily until permanently closed in September 1954. Porter Brothers Dredge worked parts of Clear, Olive, and Crane creeks in the Granite District from 1946 to 1951. The Bonnanza placer mine on Pine Creek a few miles below Cornucopia was a significant gold producer for about four years, 1986-1990. Post-war production from lode mines has been mainly from the Buffalo in the Granite District, which was reopened in 1946 and operated until 1965, and the Iron Dyke gold-copper mine and the Bay Horse silver mine on Snake River which operated in the 1980s. Many small placers and a few lode mines have produced small amounts of gold on a periodic basis. Among the latter are the Pyx (Greenhorn district), Grandview and Record (Unity district), Standard (Quartzburg district), and other similar small lode mines.

Millions of dollars have been spent in the past few decades on unsuccessful investigative attempts to reopen some of the old mines, including the E and E and the North Pole at Bourne, as well as the Cornucopia north of Halfway. More than 50,000 feet of exploratory diamond drilling was done on the Bald Mountain-Ibex vein near Bourne. Other lode mines where unsuccessful work has been done include the Buffalo, Cougar-Independence, and New York.

Gold Prices

U. S. Gold prices were long controlled by the Federal Government. The price was set at $19.393939 per fine troy in 1792, raised to $20.689658 on June 28, 1834, lowered to $20.671835 on

January 18, 1837 and raised to $35.00 on January 31, 1934. The latter price held until Government price restrictions were removed in 1974. Since that time, gold prices, although reaching a high of $800 for less than a day in the early 1980's, have generally ranged between $350 and $400 per troy ounce, until recently when prices began to exceed $600 per ounce.

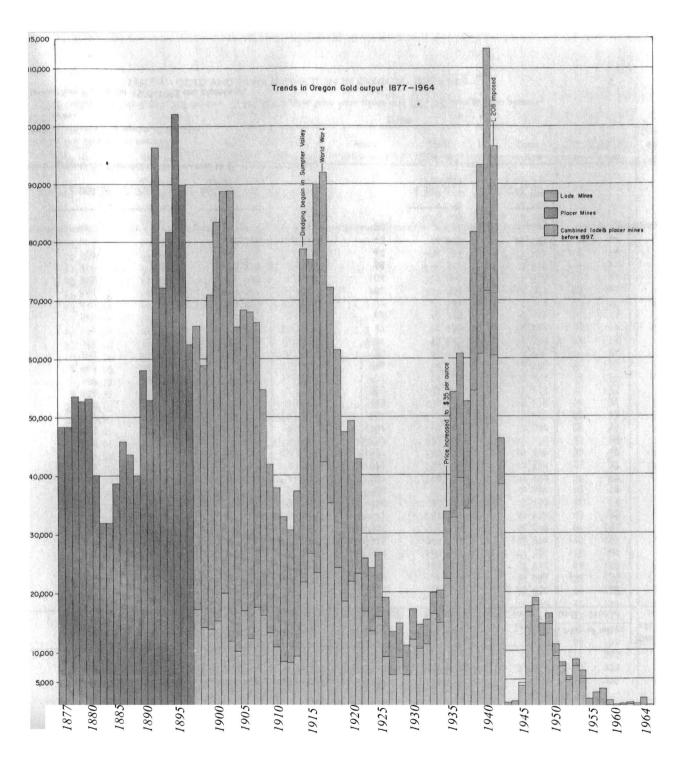

Trends in Oregon Gold Output, 1877-1964

Right: Typical miner's cabin, small, with enough room for a bed and table, and just enough logs in the wall for head clearance of the ceiling (or roof). Note the height of the shadowy miner standing in the door. Windows were rare, and often covered with rawhide, rather than glass, until shipping from east coast manufacturers increased. Heat came from a fireplace, or sometimes a purchased or homemade pot-

bellied or barrel stove, which is probably the case here, since a tin stovepipe sticks out of the roof. This particular cabin has the luxury of a large porch.. It was probably built from trees which stood where it is now standing, as evidenced by the log residue on all sides. In this photo, it is probably newly finished. The log remainders probably served as fuel for heat.

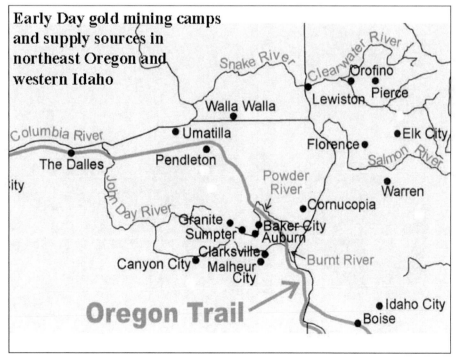

Early Day gold mining camps and supply sources in northeast Oregon and western Idaho

Gold Mining Camps along the Oregon Trail

Supplies & Transportation

Above: Steamboat Tenino on the Columbia. At least three steamboats on the Columbia ran on three sections of the river due to the need to negotiate two sets of rapid: the lower river west of Cascade Locks; the middle river, Cascade to Celilo Falls rapids above The Dalles; and the upper river above Celilo Falls to the mouth of the Snake River and on to Lewiston, Idaho. The areas between the rapids each required a separate contingent of steamboats: The portages were at first accomplished by pack train and later by a short railway. Steamboats carried 82,000 people up river as far as Lewiston in 1862. One steamboat, called the Nez Perce Chief, brought $382,000 worth of gold in one ore trip , October 7, 1862.

Right: Loaded pack train ready to haul a load of supplies cross country, perhaps to outlying mining camps. Initially, the only road was the Oregon Trail. There were no roads to the various mining camps, although once the mining began to pay, road companies formed to contract to build roads to facilitate supply deliveries.

While thousands of prospectors and miners were looking for and mining gold, many companies and individuals were implementing ways of furnishing the vast amount of food and other supplies needed by the miners.

The major sources of supplies were the Willamette Valley for farm and ranch produce and San Francisco for other supplies. The supplies were carried to Portland (then a town of 2,784, according to the 1860 census) by wagon and ship, then transferred to paddlewheel steamers for transport up the Columbia and Snake Rivers. Up river ports were The Dalles, Umatilla, Wallula, and Lewiston. From these river ports, supplies for the miners were transported overland to the mining camps. Pack strings were needed initially because most camps were in mountainous areas where roads did not exist and had to be constructed. Loads of merchandise weighing up to 250 pounds were tied to pack saddles on the backs of horses or mules and packed to the camps.

Construction of roads by the military and freight companies enabled the use of wagons and stages. Heavy freight wagons of various sizes and pulled by two to 12 teams of horses, mules, or oxen carried up to 7,500 pounds. Pack strings replaced wagons whenever roads were muddy or buried in snow, especially in winter. The cost was very much greater.

In his book, *The History of Idaho*, John Hailey gives a first hand account of the methods and expense of transporting people and the vast amounts of equipment and materials needed in the early mining camps. Hailey and William Ish were partners in Ish and Hailey Freight Co., which hauled passengers and freight from Umatilla to Boise Basin via saddle strings, pack strings, stages, and wagons. Express Ranch, established in 1862 near the present

Above: Express Ranch

site of Durkee, was a freight and stage stop on the route to Fort Boise and the Boise Basin mines. The Express Ranch post office was established April 21, 1865, with C. W. Durkee as postmaster. His name was adopted for the settlement that grew near Express Ranch. Initially, said Hailey, "We sent out a small train to the Auburn mines on Powder River in Oregon from Walla Walla about the 10th day of April, 1863, and on the 18th day of April, I left Walla Walla with a saddle train of sixteen passengers and four pack animals for Placerville in Boise Basin. This was the beginning of the saddle train business in the Boise Basin mines."

Hailey says that during 1863-1864, the first couple of years of the Boise Basin gold rush, oats retailed at fifty cents per pound in small quantities or forty cents per pound by the sack. Hay in small quantities sold at forty cents per pound and baled hay, weighing two hundred pounds or more, twenty-five cents per pound. Stable owners had hay cut from small bottoms nearby—a kind of swamp grass. This hay was baled and packed into the towns (p.63). They also had small stocks of grain packed from Oregon.

Stages moved about five miles per hour. Relay stations where horses were changed were 12 to

16

15 miles apart. Home stations where drivers changed and meals were served were 50-60 miles apart. Meals were almost uniformly bad, according to Hailey.

J.S. McClung told of his wagon train passing miners prospecting for gold in the Burnt River area on September, 16, 1862. He also wrote of tearful separations that occurred as many wagons pulled out of the train at the Auburn turnoff (Evans, p. 318). Pioneer diary entries tell of passing up to 200 freight wagons and 20 pack strings (50 to 100 animals) in

Above:Men with horses on the steep and treacherous Last Chance Road,which was used by both wagons and pack trains.

one day, coming from the Dalles bound for Auburn, a distance of 250 miles (Evans, p. 314) .

Brosnan in his *History of Idaho* says, "Many of the first gold hunters, in their eagerness to reach the mines 'hit the trail on foot.'" These pedestrians formed what was jokingly called the "Foot and Walker's Transportation Line." As early as the spring of 1863, a saddle train was in operation between the heads of navigation on the Columbia River and the Boise Basin mines. This unique agency for carrying passengers consisted usually of about twenty horses or mules. Sixteen of the animals were outfitted with riding saddles and were used for passenger transportation; while the other four animals carried baggage and provisions (p. 112).

Left: Sumpter Valley Railway log train in Picture Gorge on the Powder River.

During the following spring (1864) wagon roads were built between Umatilla and Wallula and the Boise Basin. Stage-lines then took the place of the saddle train as the chief mode of passenger transportation. The stage coaches usually were drawn by four to six horses, and carried passengers, express, "fast" freight, mail, and light baggage. Quite a few years passed before wagons replaced all the transport by pack-trains to the more remote areas. Heavy loads of merchandise were placed on the backs of horses or mules and "packed" to the mines. The work was heavy and only men of brawn and endurance were equal to the task of swinging those heavy packs upon the animal's back. The ability to fasten a load of goods securely upon a pack animal involved the mastery of the famous diamond-shaped "cinch knot'" and was considered a skilful accomplishment. After the opening of "toll" roads, the pack animal was replaced by the freight-wagon. These heavily laden, slow moving vehicles hauled great quantities of "wares of civilization" to the early mining communities and greatly reduced freight charges. The freight-wagon was usually hauled by several teams of horses, oxen, or mules. The rough weather-beaten men (and rarely women) who drove these animals became artists at "cracking" their long whips. The "freighters" who drove mules were usually known as "mule-skinners," while the ox-team drivers were given the inelegant but expressive title of "bull-whackers" (Brosnan, p.112-114).

Above: Boiler enroute to Bonanza Mine. Transporting heavy mining equipment over primitive roads sometimes required the muscle power of many animals working under the watchful eyes of experienced drovers.

River Landings

The Dalles served Canyon City and other western mining camps via The Dalles Military road. Fort Walla Walla and Umatilla served the Boise Basin and eastern Blue Mountain camps, and Lewiston served mainly the gold camps in the Clearwater and Salmon River drainages of Idaho.

In a letter to his wife dated August 17, 1862, Irving Hazeltine said that supplies for John Day's River area came from The Dalles about 200 miles away and estimated the population of the Canyon City mining camp at that time at about 1,000 persons. He said the Indian population of the area was about 80 and they were mostly peaceful (Rand, 1981).

Fort Walla Walla was established in about 1855 by the Army to maintain peace between the Indians and white settlers. Umatilla was initially a steamboat landing on the Columbia River. Lewiston was founded in 1861 on the bank of Snake River at the mouth of the Clearwater River also on Nez Perce land. It was a major supply source for miners in Clearwater and Salmon River areas from which whites were specifically excluded by treaty.

Walla Walla was a main supply source for these various gold camps and was a gathering place for miners especially those seeking refuge from the cold of winters in Idaho's high country (Florence, Elk City etc.). The Washington Statesman of Walla Walla of December 13, 1861 states, "During the week past not less than two hundred and twenty five pack animals, heavily laden with provisions, have left this city for the mines."

Charles Wilson's diary of the survey of the forty-ninth parallel, (G. F. Stanley, editor, 1970. Twin Falls, Idaho, Library) states that "the scene at Walla Walla in 1861 equals that of San Francisco, 1849, everyone in the wildest state of excitement, immense gambling houses open day and night and men ruthlessly shot down in the streets at the rate of one per diem and the place filled with all the reckless cuthroats of the far west." Walla Walla was noted for its lawlessness until a vigilance commit- tee brought about reform in 1865. The town emptied of miners when mines reopened in the spring.

In 1863, Lewiston was "the principal capital of Idaho up to which point Snake River is navigable for steamboats of light draft, thus making a continuous line of navigation from the mouth of the Columbia, with the exception of two portages at Cascades and at Celilo Falls where the river flows through the Cascade Mountains" (Campbell, 1864). There were boats above and boats below.

The first lock on the Columbia River began operating in 1896. Built by the U.S. Army Corp of Engineers, it allowed ships to move cargo upriver, eliminating the need to portage goods around the Cascade rapids. After the completion of the Bonneville Dam and Lock, the rapids and the Cascades Canal and Lock were submerged.

Above, until the advent of the railroad, horses, mules and oxen were the primary modes of transportation, as in the classic Hazeltine photo above, taken on Front Street of Baker City, showing a family with a very mixed team.

Below, a Sumpter street scene, with a 9 two-horse and mule teams hitched to a wagon carrying a steam boiler destined for an area mine.

Above: Ten-man mine crew posing for a picture.

Law and Order

Most mining camps were rough and tumble places where saloons and bordellos outnumbered other types of business. Each had its share of murders, robberies, and other sorts of lawlessness. But most early settlers were industrious, intelligent, and forward-looking people who maintained their sense of morality and justice in those exciting times. They recognized the need for law and order to keep the peace and protect property rights. New camps made their own rules and elected officials by majority vote. Local governments, schools, and churches were soon established.

The first law in new mining camps was the mining code established to govern the location of mining claims. The first official was the claims recorder, shortly after came sheriffs and judges to keep the peace and protect property rights, all being chosen by vote of the miners. The establishment of mining districts with their rules and regulations helped bring law and order to the Oregon Territory. Many of the present rules governing water rights date from these early miners' regulations.

The basic principles of today's mining laws were established by Congressional Act of July 26, 1866, and revised in 1872. Presently a lode-mining claim is limited to a length of 1,500 feet and width of 600 feet. Placer claims are limited to 20 acres and most are located by legal subdivision, although odd shaped claims of 20 acres or less are acceptable. Any U.S. citizen may locate or otherwise own any number of either or both lode or placer claims on unclaimed public domain. For claims to be legal each must encompass a "discovery" of valuable mineral in place. Annually thereafter, the owner must do at least $100 worth of work at each claim for the claim to remain valid.

Law and order in terms of personal safety was often the product of several citizens agreeing to form a jury, with one among them appointed as judge. For example, in 1862, two men newly arrived in Auburn became ill. According to Isaac Hiatt, in *31 Years in Baker County*, Dr. Rackerby pronounced that the man in the tent had all the symptoms of strychnine poisoning, and a second was ill with similar problems. The antidote the doctor gave saved one of the men. When a piece of bread from the breakfast table was tossed to a dog, it soon had convulsions and died, which convinced the people that it was premeditated murder. The blame was placed on the third member of the party, Lucien Garnier. Lacking any civil authority, a people's court convicted Lucien Gasnier of murder and executed him on September 19, 1862 (pp. 21-22).

Also, the Auburn cemetery contains the still-readable tombstones of Jack Desmond and H.M. Larabee who were stabbed and killed on November 18, 1862, by a ruffian known as "Spanish Tom." By Hiatt's account, Spanish Tom was later tracked down in Mormon Basin and brought back to Auburn, where he was handed over to George Hall, who had been appointed sheriff. Although Sheriff Hall attempted to keep the prisoner safe and give him due process of law, a mob seized Spanish Tom and hanged without judge or jury (pp.33-34).

Similarly, according to Isaac Hiatt, in 1864 Boggs Greenwood killed a man named Kinear. Then Greenwood and his gang stopped at Express Ranch (near present-day Durkee). There Greenwood shot and wounded a Mr. Cox who was trying to protect Mrs. Durkee from the gang. A posse caught Greenwood near Straw Ranch, northwest of Express Ranch and hanged him without judge or jury (pp. 81-82). A Justice of the Peace had been appointed, starting October 29, 1862, but apparently in those early times, the violent act of murder was dealt with harshly and with little delay.

Land Claims and Mining Claims

In the early days of western settlement, government policies encouraged the transfer of western lands to private ownership. Among Congressional acts under which farm and ranch lands could have been acquired were the Pre-emption Land Claims Act of 1838, the Donation Land Claim Act of 1850, or the Homestead Act of 1862. Among the earliest land claims in eastern Oregon were the Express Ranch (Durkee) and Miller Ranch (Huntington) in the fall of 1862, and Straw Ranch (Pleasant Valley), date uncertain. Enactment of the Homestead Act resulted in a rush for farm and ranch land as well as for gold.

Prior to 1866, there were no Federal or Territorial laws governing the acquisition, size, or manner of recording mining property. Such rules as existed were self-imposed by the miners themselves in each of the mining districts. Those rules varied somewhat from camp to camp, but the rules, adopted by majority vote, were generally adhered to because the miners were forced, for selfish reasons, to do so in order to maintain peace and property rights. Probably initially miners fought over property but soon realized that before anyone's right to property could be protected all property rights had to be protected.

Above: Miners underground at Blue Bird Mine in Red Boy District, working by candlelight drilling blast holes in rock containing quartz veins (the white streaks) with hand-held steel drills and sledgehammers. Miners typically worked 8-10 hours a day, often under uncomfortable and dangerous conditions. Many were injured or killed by such events as falling rock, cave-ins or misfired dynamite charges. Note cloth headgear. Hard hats were a thing of the future. Miners gained some protection by boiling their cloth hats in wax.

The Gold Producing Belt

The gold producing belt is about 120 miles long and 40 miles wide extending from John Day east to the Snake River in the southeastern part of the Blue Mountains. The principle mining districts are in the Powder, John Day, and Burnt River drainage areas of Baker and Grant Counties. Parts of some districts extend into adjacent parts of Malheur and Union Counties. Within this belt are innumerable placer mines, at least 14 lode mines having production records of more than $1,000,000 worth of gold, dozens more that produced between $100,000 and $1,000,000, and hundreds of prospects where gold has been found in quantities too small to pay for mining.

The largest concentration of both lode and placer mines is in the vicinity of Sumpter, Granite, and Greenhorn west of Baker City. Five adjoining mines on the North Pole Columbia Lode at Bourne produced about $8,000,000 in 1895-1916. The Bonanza, Red Boy, and Buffalo mines each produced $1,000,000 or more. The Buffalo operated almost continuously between 1903 and 1965.

The largest lode mine in the gold belt, the Cornucopia, 10 miles north of Halfway produced more than $10,000,000 (and maybe much more) in gold and silver between 1884 and 1941 from underground workings totaling 36 miles in length. Other large lode mines in the gold belt, their approximate production, and the years they were operated include: The Ben Harrison on the West Fork of Clear Creek (1913-1914, 1916-1920, 1926-1928,1936-1937); the Baisley-Elkhorn on the North Fork of Pine Creek northwest of Baker City ($937,000, 1882-1912), the Highland-Maxwell two miles west of the Baisley-Elkhorn ($475,000, 1900-1938), the Sanger north of Sparta ($1,500,000 pre-1900); the Connor Creek mine on Connor Creek north of Huntington ($1,125,000, l880-l890 and 1915-1918); and the Rainbow ($2,323,092, 1901-1919) and Humboldt ($225,000, 1909-1915) in northern Malheur County; The Iron Dyke mine at Homestead produced about $12,000,000 in copper and gold during 1915-1928 and the 1980's.

Geology of the Blue Mountains Gold Belt

Rocks exposed in the gold belt of the Blue Mountains are divisible into three groups based on when, where, and how they were formed.

1. **Metamorphosed marine sedimentary, volcanic, and intrusive rocks**
This oldest group of rocks was formed on and beneath the floor of an ancient ocean and were pushed against to become part of the North American continent as part of the process called plate tectonics. These rocks range from Early Pennsylvanian to Late Jurassic in age, which covers the span of geologic time between about 300 million and 150 million years ago. Rocks formed during parts of Permian, Late Triassic and Middle Jurassic ages appear to be the most widely exposed. Included are ocean floor sedimentary rocks, chiefly argillite and chert, lava flows and tuffaceous rocks erupted from volcanoes on the ocean floor (mostly basalt and andesite), and igneous rocks (serpentinite, gabbro, and diorite), which formed from magma that came from deep within the earth and congealed in great cracks in the ocean floor. These rocks are metamorphosed to greenschist facies, which means that their original mineralogy and structure changed as a result of the deep burial and the intense folding and faulting they underwent while being pushed against the continent.

The Paleozoic to Late Jurassic marine sedimentary, volcanic, and intrusive rocks have been divided into four terranes. The work of many authors is summarized by Brooks (1979), including Brooks and others (1976); Vallier and others (1977); Brooks and Vallier (1978); Dickinson and Thayer (1978). The terranes were later named the Wallowa, Baker, Izee, and Olds Ferry terranes by Silberling and others (1984). All of the terranes may relate to a single allochthonous island arc (Vallier and Brooks, 1986).

The Wallowa and Olds Ferry Terranes are volcanic island-arc fragments made up mainly of arc-type volcanic rocks with interlayerd fossiliferous volcaniclastic sedimentary rocks. The Wallowa Terrane includes the Clover Creek Greenstone named by Gilluly (1937) for the exposures on Clover Creek in the Baker 30-minute quadrangle, and in the Wallowa Mountains. Similar rocks in adjacent Snake River Canyon were named the Seven Devils Volcanics by Anderson (1930). Vallier (1977) changed the name to Seven Devils Group and included four formations: from oldest to youngest, the Lower Permian Windy Ridge and Hunsaker Creek Formations, and the Middle and Upper Triassic Wild Sheep Creek and Doyle Creek Formations. The Olds Ferry terrane is composed of volcanic and volcaniclastic rocks of the upper Triassic Huntington Formation. Whether the Wallowa and Olds Ferry terranes are parts of the same or different arcs is not clear. There are slight differences in rock

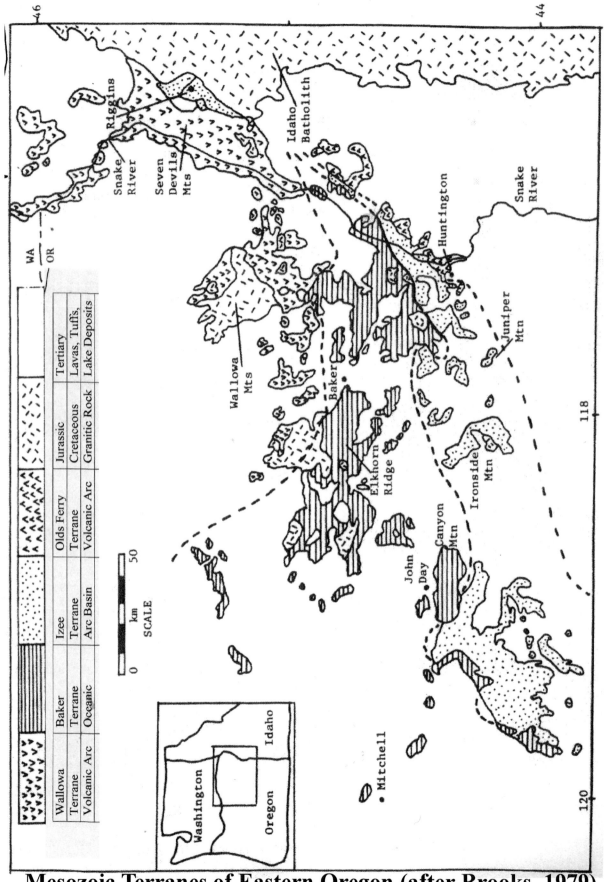

Mesozoic Terranes of Eastern Oregon (after Brooks, 1979)

composition and age.

The Baker Terrane is comprised of severly disrupted and metamorphosed volcanic and ocean basin sedimentary rock assemblages including the Elkhorn Ridge Argillite and Burnt River Schist formations and large and small fault blocks of volcanic rocks and mafic and untramafic intrusive rocks correlative with the Canyon Mountain Complex. Blocks of serpentinite and serpentinite matrix melanges are widely distributed.

The Elkhorn Ridge Argillite is described by Brooks and others (1982) and Ferns and others (1987) as deformed sedimentary complex composed mainly of dark colored siliceous argillite, argillite and chert with small amounts of black carbonaceous argillite, bedded silicic tuff, ribbon chert, sandstone, conglomerate and small limestone bodies. Ribbon chert samples have yielded microfossils of Permian and Late Triassic age. Permian fusulinids have been found in one of many small limestone bodies. Localities where fossils have been found are extremely rare. Schistose sedimentary and volcanic rocks exposed along the lower part of Burnt River and adjacent Snake River in the southeastern part of the terrane have been mapped as part of the Burnt River Schist.

Rocks of the Izee Terrane are mostly clastic sedimentary rocks, volcanic greywacke, siltstone and minor conglomerate and limestone of Late Triassic to Middle Jurassic age. Small limestone bodies occur locally. Rocks in the western part of the terrane south and southwest of John Day have been subdivided into about 25 different formations ranging from Late Triassic to Late Jurassic age. In the eastern part of the terrane the rocks are so lithologically similar and fossils so rare that subdivision is not possible. Fossils found range from Early to Middle Jurassic age.

All rocks of the four terranes have been metamorphosed to the green schist facies. Some relation-ships between the terranes that appear plausible are (1) rocks of the Izee terrane were deported on already disrupted strata of the Baker Terrane; (2) part of the Izee terrane was derived from erosion of volcanic rocks of the Olds Ferry terrane. The Izee clastic terrane was deposited in a basin that covered the contact between the Baker Melange Terrane and tne Huntington Arc Terrane. The terranes must have been amalgamated in pre-Late Jurassic time, because they are pinned together by Late Jurassic-Early Cretaceous granitic intrusive bodies.

2. **Late Jurassic-Cretaceous Granitic Rocks**

Granitic rocks are exposed in several areas of the gold belt. Large granitic bodies are called batholiths; smaller ones are called stocks. The Wallowa Batholith forms the core of the Wallowa Mountains and the Bald Mountain Batholith underlies a large part of Elkhorn Ridge. The granitic rocks formed from magma that invaded the ancient metamorphic rocks about 120 to 130 million years ago during Late Jurassic-Early Cretaceous time. The granitic rocks range widely in composition from aplite to diorite. Most bodies are largely quartz diorite or granodiorite.

3. **Tertiary Continental Rocks**

Tertiary rocks, which locally cover the ancient metamorphic and granitic rocks, are mainly lava flows, tuffaceous rocks and sedimentary deposits, the latter having formed in fresh water lakes and river-floodplains. The lavas and tuffs range in composition from basalt to rhyolite and are mostly Miocene and Pliocene age. The lake deposits are composed largely of tuffaceous sediment. The

26

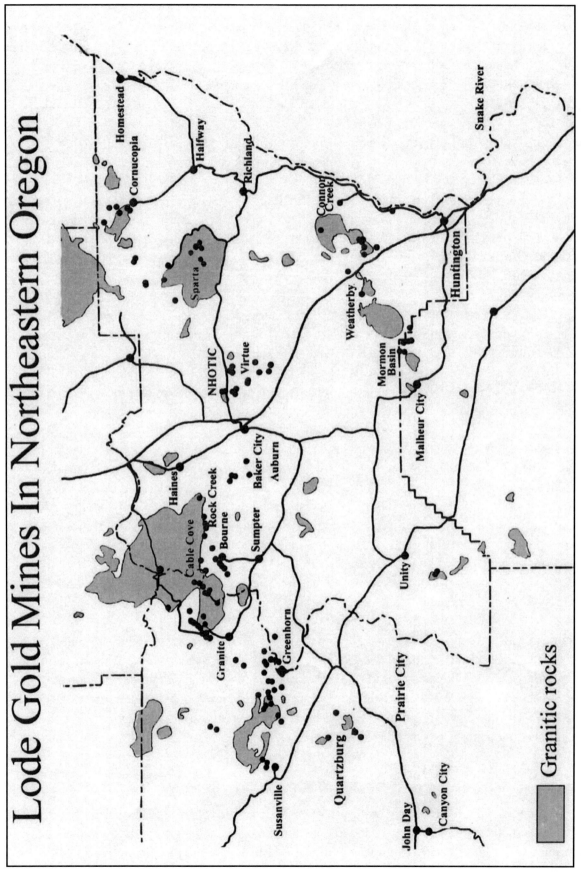

Lode Gold Mines In Northeastern Oregon

Granitic rocks

The maps on pages 24 and 26 should be viewed together. The map on page 24 shows the distribution of Pre Tertiary rock exposures. The map on page 26 shows the granitic rock exposure plus the location (black dots) of many vein-type gold deposits that typically occur near the edges of the intrusions. The forceful intrusion of the extremely hot granitic magma is believed to have furnished the heat and fluids that formed the gold deposits and the fracture zones in which they are found. See text on page 27.

Tertiary rocks are not metamorphosed and, therefore, generally are easily distinguished from the old metamorphosed oceanic rocks. During much of the Cretaceous and early Tertiary time (150 to 30 million years ago), the area that is eastern Oregon underwent a period of erosion in which the ancient metamorphic and granitic rocks were deeply eroded. For much of that time the landscape probably was mountainous, similar to that of today.

Characteristics of the Gold Deposits

There are two main types of gold deposits: lode deposits and placer deposits. In lode deposits the gold is in solid rock that must be dug out of the ground and processed to collect the gold. In placer deposits the gold occurs as loose flakes and nuggets that were eroded from solid rock and deposited in surficial accumulations of weathered rock, chiefly gravel, sand, and silt.

Lode Deposits

Most of the lode deposits are associated with tabular (sheet like) veins in rocks of the Baker terrane. A few deposits in the Wallowa terrane are of volcanogenic origin. An example of the latter-type deposit is the Iron Dyke Mine in the Homestead district, Oregon's largest copper producer. The veins usually consist mainly of quartz, altered rock, and small amounts of metallic gold and silver and other metallic minerals, chiefly the sulfides of iron, copper, lead, zinc, and locally arsenic. Tellurides of gold and silver occur in a few mines, for example the Cornucopia Mine and mines along the North Pole Columbia Lode. Silver sulfide minerals were found in several mines.

The veins are clustered near the edges of Jurassic-Cretaceous granitic intrusive rocks and are associated with fracture zones along faults in the earth's crust. The fracture zones provided open spaces for the deposition of the ore minerals derived from hot circulating fluids and gases generated during the emplacement and cooling of the intrusive bodies. The veins occur in both the intrusive rocks and the older rocks bordering the intrusive. The older, intruded, rocks in most districts include metamorphosed argillite, chert, sandstone and siltstone and/or volcanic rocks. Gabbro, diorite and serpentinite are included in a few areas.

To obtain the gold from veins, miners drilled and blasted shafts and tunnels deep into the ground, dug out the gold-bearing rock, hauled it to the surface where it was crushed and ground and then milled or shipped to a smelter to recover the gold. Equipment used to do the mining and milling was expensive and the work was dangerous.

There are thousands of quartz veins in the rocks of northeastern Oregon that have been investigated by prospectors. Most are too small or contain too little gold or silver per ton of rock to sustain a profitable mining operation. The relatively few veins that have produced significant amounts of gold and silver ranged from a few inches to tens of feet wide and from hundreds of feet in length to the extraordinary 4.5 miles length of the North Pole Columbia Lode. The greatest depth of mining attained was 2,500 feet below the highest outcrop of the veins, also at the North Pole Columbia lode.

Gold content of mined ore averaged between 1/2 and 1 ounce per ton, although many veins contained pockets of very rich ore. The veins were rarely uniform in value and many were too small or contain insufficient values to be mineable. The parts of veins that contain valuable minerals in mineable quantity are called "ore shoots" or "ore bodies." For example, although the North Pole

Columbia Lode is 4.5 miles long, gold production has been confined to a 12,000 feet long section in the central part of the lode. Although some ore bodies were mined continuously along the strike for many hundreds of feet, most of them were interrupted at irregular intervals by zones too lean to pay for mining. In northeastern Oregon few ore bodies attained mineable widths of more than 10 feet and most averaged less than 4 feet. Most were steeply dipping and therefore could be extracted economically only by underground mining.

At well-managed mines high grade and low grade ores are mixed and blended thus extending the life of the mine. Leaving sub grade ore in a mine is considered by most mine operators a waste of a non-renewable resource. The parts of veins that are barren of gold are identified by assaying and the material is either left in place or mined and hauled to the waste dump on the surface or is used to back-fill already mined areas underground.

Above: Miner operating a stoper, drilling blast holes in a vein that dips about 45 degrees in the Ben Harrison Mine. Blast hole drilling became much faster and easier when compressed air drills came into use in the 1890s. Unfortunately, the early drills of this type produced a cloud of dust that when breathed by miners tended to cause a lethal disease called silicosis. The problem was solved later when holes were made in the center of the drillrods and water was forced to the bottom of the drill hole, thus making slurry of the drill cuttings that was washed out of the drill hole.

*Arrastra ruins at a
northeastern Oregon mine.*

Milling Equipment

Arrastra

The Arrastra was a primitive devise used to grind gold bearing rock by dragging heavy stones or concrete blocks over crushed ore spread on a circular bed of stones or concrete. They were built mostly of wood. The waterwheel turned a vertical spindle with arms that were attached by chain or cable to heavy stones which were dragged over crushed ore spread on a circular bed of smooth stones or concrete. The bed was encircled by a concrete wall a few inches to about two feet high.

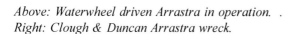

*Above: Waterwheel driven Arrastra in operation. .
Right: Clough & Duncan Arrastra wreck.*

THE MEXICAN MILL

The Arrastre, or Mexican Mill, operated through power from an overshot water wheel. This power was transmitted through a rack and pinion to four rotating arms. Large granite boulders chained to the arms crushed the ore.

Stamp mill

The stamp mill uses rows of heavy iron pestles (stamps) which are mechanically lifted and dropped on crushed ore that is fed into a huge iron mortar standing on a concrete block. The stamps, each weighing several hundred pounds are lifted and dropped 6 or 8 inches one hundred or more times a minute. The flat surfaces in front of the stamps are plates made of copper and coated with mercury. Water washes the pulverized ore across the plates. Gold amalgamates with the mercury and is later recovered from the amalgam by distilling off the mercury.

Above: Stamp mill. Interior of Bald Mountain Mine mill. Stamps and tables behind the man. Upper center is the large belt driven flywheel that turns the cam shaft that lifts and drops the stamps.

Flotation

Flotation is a milling process by which different minerals in finely ground ore are separated on the basis of whether they sink or float when fed into cells, usually tub-like, filled with water treated with certain chemicals then agitated to form a froth. The froth floats the valuable minerals off from the top of the cell while the waste material sinks and is drawn off at the bottom. *(See page 97 for photo of flotation cells in operation.)*

Left: Men scraping amalgam from copper plates.

Amalgamation tables.

This advertisement, which appeared in "Eastern Oregon's Gold Fields," a souvenir edition of Baker City's Morning Democrat, May 20, 1898, shows a cutaway of what the inner workings of a mining mill looked like.

Assay Office

Above: Arthur Woodwell in his assay office.

Every mine of consequence had an assay office to analyze samples to determine the quality of products from the mine and mill.

Arthur Woodwell was among the most highly respected independent assayers. His laboratory was in the front part of his home in Sumpter. He was often called upon to check the accuracy of other laboratories. He was also an accomplished surveyor. My recollection of what he told me in the late 1950's is that he moved to the Sumpter area in 1911 at the age of 18 and was on the job trained as assayer and surveyor.

Above: Panama Placer with sluice box and man with a gold pan.. Writing on photo says, "A cleanup at Panama Placer."

Humboldt Placer, Canyon City area. Chinese carrying rocks in a sling. Writing on the photo says "Each year $15,000 to $17,000. Mine worked 20 years."

Placer Deposits

In placer deposits the gold occurs as grains, flakes, and nuggets in stream bed gravel deposits. The gold was eroded from exposed vein deposits and washed downhill to where it accumulated in streambeds, flood plains, and gulches.

Placer mine near Dayville

Mining required excavation of the gravel deposits and separating the gold from the gravel. Because gold is much heavier than the typical accompanying rock debris, it rapidly works downward during agitation. Running water is nearly always used to wash away the rock debris, leaving the much heavier gold behind.

Workable gold placers usually lie in or near districts where gold-bearing veins occur. Thus, the tracing of placer gold uphill to its source has led to the discovery of important lode mines.

Early day placer mining methods were labor intensive, utilizing equipment that prospectors could carry on their backs or on pack horses or mules such as gold pans, shovels, and picks or that they could make of wood with simple tools at the mine site such as rockers, cradles, and sluice boxes.

Generally, only parts of auriferous gravel deposits are rich enough to be worked profitably. The "pay streaks" are commonly very irregular and have to be located by hit-and-miss prospecting. Gold may be transported long distances by water, but as a rule the greater the distance from the source the finer and more scattered it becomes and the more rounded or flattened are the particles. The general run of gold recovered from placers ranges in size from that of a mustard seed to a wheat grain.

U.S. Bank Gold

Imagine the excitement when early-day prospectors using picks, shovels and gold pans found nuggets in a stream bank similar to the ones pictured on the next page. Gold was worth $20.67 per troy ounce and $20.00 would buy four pairs of good shoes. Today gold is worth $600 per ounce and will buy 4 pairs of good shoes

The largest gold nugget, weighing 80.5 ounces troy, was found in 1913 at Susanville in Grant County. The nugget is worth about $25,000. but the bank wouldn't sell for that because its value as a collector's item or museum piece is far greater than its metal content. The largest nugget recorded in eastern Oregon contained 677.31 ounces of gold.

Streams continually change course or disappear entirely as erosion and orogenic movements alter the configuration of the earth's surface. Thus, gold-bearing gravels may be found on the sides or even the tops of hills far from present drainages. Graveled terraces or "high bars" along valley walls may mark the former levels of streams. Old gravels may be buried by lava, by glacial or landslide debris, or by gravels from rejuvenated streams. Gravels long buried may become firmly cemented and thus prove difficult to work with ordinary placer-mining methods.

Gold may become so finely divided that several thousand "colors" may be required to equal the value of one dollar. In such condition it is extremely difficult to "save" by any known method of placer mining that is of a sufficiently large scale to be profitable.

At the other extreme, many nuggets the size of chicken eggs or larger have been won from Oregon placer deposits. Lindgren states that a nugget worth $14,000 (at $20.67 per ounce) was reportedly discovered in McNamee Gulch in the Greenhorn district of western Baker County. Such a nugget would be equivalent to 677.31 ounces of pure gold (1901, p. 636).

GOLD DISPLAY
U.S. National Bank of Oregon
BAKER, ORE. BRANCH

Above: Postcard of gold display.

The Armstrong nugget, weighing 80 ounces troy, was found in 1913 at Susanville in Grant County. It is on display at the United States National Bank of Oregon branch in Baker City along with many other specimens of both lode and placer gold. The value of large nuggets as collector's items or museum pieces are often worth more than twice the value of their metal content.

Right: Wilbur King pans for gold in Powder River.

Placer Mining Equipment

Placer deposits typically were found by prospectors using gold pans, picks, and shovels which most prospectors carried with them. Later came the use of the sluice box and the rocker that could be made easily by hand at the mine site. After the bonanza placers began to reach exhaustion and better equipment was brought to the mines, the lower grade, but usually much more extensive deposits were worked by a system called "hydraulicking." Much later came the use of giant dredges that churned thousands of acres into wastelands but recovered large amounts of gold.

Right: Gold pan with flakes of gold.

Gold Pan and Sluice

The gold pan was the prospector's best tool for testing gravel to see if there was gold in it. If there was he would pan samples of gravel from all parts of the deposit to get an idea how much gold might be available. If the deposit were rich enough he might make a little money panning. A good panner could do 50 pans in a day. If he got 10 cents per pan that is $5.00 per day which was pretty good wages in the early days. The next step was building and setting up a sluice box which could handle much more gravel than panning. Some deposits were mined by tunneling under barren gravels and soil, wheeling out pay dirt, and running it through sluice boxes. The pay dirt under the barren gravel and soil might be a few inches to several feet deep. At many deposits some of the richest ground was within a few inches of bedrock, often in cracks and crevices in the bedrock. Stories are told of miners using spoons and knife blades and sometimes a little dynamite to extract coarse gold from bedrock cracks and crevices.

A sluice box or sluice is a slightly inclined wooden trough with cleats nailed across the bottom. Gravel is washed through the box; the gold sinks to the bottom of the moving gravel and is trapped by the cleats.

A rocker, is a short sluice box with a superimposed detachable sieve for screening out waste material. A rocking motion usually supplied by hand aids in separating the gold from the waste rock.

Right: Large sluice

Above: Building a flume or sluice through the forest.

Left: A sluice built across old mine tailings. Damaged photo.

Hydraulic Placer Mining

Nelson Placer on Salmon Creek west of Baker City is an example of hydraulic mining of gold-bearing gravel deposits. A large volume of water run through a system of ditches and pipes then forced through a nozzle under great pressure is used to break down gravel of stream beds and wash it through sluice boxes where the gold is extracted. Mining has exposed bedrock in places. This mine produced about $400,000 worth of gold prior to 1916. Hydraulic mining was outlawed in California in 1884 because large volumes of silt and sand were being washed out into the fertile valleys and destroying rich farmland.

Nelson Placer pit.

Archie Downie Placer.
(Near Sumpter)

Dredging

Bucketline dredges were the most efficient method of working large acreages of placer gravel. They cost a lot to build but operating costs were only a few cents per yard. Dredges operated in various parts of the region between 1913 and 1954. Collectively, they produced about 480,000 ounces of gold which at that time was worth about $12.5 million but at today's prices is worth about $168,000,000. At times during those years annual gold production from dredges exceeded that year's production of all the lode mines combined. Bucketline dredges operated in Sumpter Valley below Sumpter, in Canyon Creek and on the John Day River near John Day, along the Middle Fork of the John Day below Bates and at Susanville, on Granite, Clear, and Bull Run Creeks in the Granite area, on Burnt River near Whitney, and on Clarks Creek and Burnt River near Bridgeport. Sumpter dredge No. 3, now the centerpiece of the Sumpter Dredge State Park, is the last of three dredges that operated in Sumpter Valley from 1913 to 1954. Sumpter Valley is the largest dredge field in Oregon. Combined, the three dredges covered 2,603 acres, mined 60,000,000 yards of gravel and produced 296,906 ounces of gold and 71,000 ounces of silver worth at today's prices about $80,000,000.

Left: Sumpter Dredge No. 3 operating in Sumpter Valley. Gravel was picked up by the chain of buckets and run through a gravity separation plant inside the barge, where the gold was separated from it, and then the gravel was discharged behind the boat by a long continuous belt.

Right: Close up of the bucket line. The dredge was a Yuba-Electric, equipped with 72 nine-cubic-foot buckets. It dug to an average depth of 18 feet. Between 20 and 30 men were employed. Except for a three-year shutdown during World War II, this dredge operated almost continuously through September 1954.

Two views of Sumpter area dredges, showing the dredge pond created by the dredge, and the tailing piles that cover about 2,600 acres .

Above: Aerial photo of part of the 2600 acres of dredge tailings of Sumpter Valley.

Below: Sumpter Dredge tailings today. Vegetation is slowly returning.

Ditches

Most methods of extracting gold from placer gravel required the use of running water. Parts of most, and all of some, gold-bearing gravel deposits were found in areas where water was unavailable or scarce such as hillsides, ridges, and dry gulches. For that reason many ditches, some of great length, were constructed. Some were built along steep hillsides and collected water from all of the streams crossed by the ditch. The Auburn ditch was completed in 1863. Sparta and Eldorado ditches in 1873. The Eldorado Ditch (called Burnt River Ditch until 1872-1873) was extended headward by increments over a period of ten years (1862?-1873) and eventually carried water from as far as the head of the South Fork of Burnt River, more than 100 miles, to the placers of Malheur area. It has been called the longest placer mining ditch dug in the US. The Eldorado Ditch, built mostly by Chinese labor, was 8½ feet wide at the top, 6 feet wide at the bottom, and 3 feet deep. Use of the water carried by the ditch was the subject of many arguments and a few fights (no record of serious injuries) and lawsuits between the miners and Burnt River and Willow Creek Valley ranchers. After about 1873, the ditch was extended on past Amelia in northern Malheur County to Discovery Gulch (about 12 miles).

Use of these ditches for mining ceased long ago. The Auburn ditch is now part of the Baker City municipal water system. The Sparta ditch is used for irrigation. Hog'em ditch (sometimes spelled Hogum), 12 miles long, which included part of Phillips-Engle ditch, was built in 1864. Hog'em dumps into Goose Creek, and furnishes water to Hutton and other ranches on Goose Creek. Hog'em ditch is also part of the old Sparta Ditch.

Campbell mentions one ditch 12 miles long built at a cost of $50,000 (vol. 700 inches) which sold water for 75 cents per inch.

Placer ditch under construction.

The People—Who Were They?

The new miners and settlers were mostly young Caucasian men, led by experienced miners from California gold fields, made most of the new discoveries. Most traveled in groups for safety. Many prospectors and miners were greenhorns with dreams of getting rich but often were poorly equipped. A few became wealthy but most arrived too late and found that all the good claims had been taken. The reason for each successive "rush" was to get there before all the good claims were being mined. The late comers worked for others or moved on looking for gold elsewhere. Many eventually returned to their homes and families disillusioned and broke.

An exception was Columbus Sewel, an African American man who worked as a drayman, raising a family in the Canyon City and John Day area in the early days (mentioned in Helen Rand's book *Whiskey Gulch*). Rand says that Sewel came to the area with Bradford C. Trowbridge during the early days of the gold rush. Trowbridge, George Irving Hazeltine and Billy Wilson purchased a piece of land bordering the present fair grounds. Trowbridge bought out Wilson and Hazeltine and with Sewel's help developed the Trowbridge Ranch in 1862, the first and oldest ranch in Grant County.

Whiskey Gulch is composed mostly of letters written by her grandfather, George Irving Hazeltine, to his bride, Emeline McCallum. The two were wed in April, 1862. The letters provide interesting documentation of life of the times, as mentioned incidentally in the letters. In a letter to his wife dated August 17, 1862, Irving Hazeltine said that supplies for the John Day River area came from The Dalles about 200 miles away. Hazeltine estimated the population at that time at about 1,000 persons (Rand 1981).

Right: A carefully dressed couple pose in front of their tent house in a mining camp. Note on photo says "Temporary camp of the Jas. B. Sipe Mining Co. July 30, 1908."

Above: Horse logging. Pioneers needed lumber for houses and other buildings. Cutting and hauling logs, then sawing them into useable lumber was slow, labor intensive, and dangerous work.

Right: Bald Mountain Mine boarding house and barn in deep snow. Photo illustrates difficult winter conditions encountered by northeastern Oregon miners, where winters were harsh with snow, ice, and temperatures below freezing. James Virtue recorded in his 1864 diary his walks up and over Dooley Mountain from Clarksville to Auburn in winter. On one of them he froze his feet, requiring several days of recovery before he could return to his "snowshoes" for the return trip to Clarksville.

Schools

The communities that were established soon set up schools for the children of the area. James Evans' Gold Dust & Chalk Dust gives the following list of school districts that were established in Baker County by 1876: (1) Auburn, 1862; (2) Pocahontas,1862-63; (3) James (near Auburn), 1863; (4) Wingville, 1864; Baker (then known as Powderville), 1865; (6) Mt Carmel (near North Powder), 1865; (7) Rock Creek, 1866; (8) Ebell Creek, 1867; (9) Rye Valley, 1870; (10) Bridgeport, 1873; (11) Fairview (north of Baker), 1874; (12) Pleasant Valley, 1876. Others established by 1899 were (13) Lookout; (14) Troy; (15) Weatherby; (16) Huntington; (17) Muddy Creek; (18)

Auburn School

McEwen; (19) Plano; (20) Hereford; (23) Home; (24) Haines. Evans further says that of these communities, one-third were supported mainly by mining, one-third by farming, and one-third by transportation (stage stops, ferries, road companies, etc.).

Native Indians

"Indians of the northwest bitterly resented the devastating effect the thousands of miners searching for gold had on the pristine hunting grounds, streams, and meadows they had roamed freely upon for thousands of years. Deer, elk, bear and rabbits were killed for food or chased away by the miners. Rivers and streams were muddied by mine operations and the fish destroyed. Prairies and meadowlands were turned into farms and ranches. This encroachment on traditional tribal lands by miners and the settlers who followed led to armed conflicts between the Indians and the U. S. Army during the 1850's-1870's which constituted the final major steps in the long but inevitable destruction of the nomadic way of life for the American Indians" (Lapwai Reservation information pamphlet). The government forced the Indians onto reservations a small fraction of the size of original tribal lands and declared the remaining lands open for settlement by whites.

Some of the tribes included were the Shoshone, Bannock, Umatilla, Paiute and Nez Perce. The Nez Perce was the tribe most affected by gold discoveries in Idaho and northeast Oregon. It was the Nez Perce who had helped Lewis and Clark early in the century. Britton says, "In September 1805 Lewis and Clark estimated the Nez Perce tribe's population at 7,600. However, by 1829 as noted by John McLaughlin, Chief Factor for the Hudson's Bay Company at Fort Vancouver, as many as seven-eighths of all Pacific Coast Indians had died from small pox, ague, and other diseases spread by sexual intercourse with the maritime fur trade sailors. In 1835, Samuel Parker, a representative of the American Board of Commissioners For Foreign Missions, thought that the Nez Perce tribe had declined to 2,500. By the 1860's the tribe had increased to 3,700 at which point it stabilized." (p. 25). Nez Perce were avid farmers (p. 23). In 1862 the tribe had 2,000 acres of fenced and tilled soil on which they raised a large variety of vegetables, fruits, and grains. They owned 50,000 horses (13 horses per individual) and 2,000 cows" (1888, p. 16).

According to Brosnan, the Treaty of 1855 was negotiated by General Isaac I. Stevens. Indians agreed to sell their lands. Following that, the Treaty of 1863 took the Wallowa Valley from old Chief Joseph and reduced the size of the reservation at Lapwai. In the spring of 1877, the Wallowa band of Nez Perce was ordered by Washington, D.C., officials to go onto the Lapwai Reservation. Several battles ensued, during which Chief Joseph's band began its famous 1,300 mile trek toward Canada (from Wallowa Valley to Lo Lo Pass, Idaho to Bear Paw Mountain, Montana). Joseph surrendered October 4, 1877. Gen. Miles promised him that he and his band would be returned to Lapwai Reservation but instead they were sent to Fort Leavenworth, Kansas, then to Indian Territory, Oklahoma, and finally to the Colville Reservation. near Spokane (Brosnan, 134+).

Earlier, General John Ellis Wool, acting on his belief that civilian treatment of the Indians was unfair, issued an order on August 7, 1856, forbidding settlement east of the Cascades in the area he regarded as "Indian Country." That area is now the eastern parts of Oregon and Washington. The order stated: "No emigrants or other whites, except the Hudson's Bay Company, or persons having ceded rights from the Indians, will be permitted to settle or remain in the Indian country, or on land not ceded by treaty, confirmed by the Senate, and approved by the President of the United States." Miners in the Colville area were excluded from the order. Wool was soon replaced (Ontko, v. 2, p. 283) and the order was rescinded.

Buffalo Bill with Sells-Floto Circus in Baker City in 1914. Other than such performing troupes, Native Americans were seldom seen in Baker County after the turn of the century.

As more miners and settlers moved in, Indian troubles accelerated. Colonel E. J. Steptoe, who was in command at Fort Walla Walla, set out with 159 men to investigate the murder of two miners by a party of Palouse Indians near the Hudson's Bay Company's post at Fort Colville the spring of 1858. He encountered a force of 1200 "savages" (Coeur d'Alene, Palouse, Spokane, and Yakima tribes.) The two groups fought all day, then stole away at night. That fight became known as the Battle of Steptoe Butte (near Rosalia, Washington). Later, Col. Wright hanged several Palouses who were proved guilty of the murder of some miners (exact date unknown but sometime in late 1858).

The gold mining camps established in Idaho's Clearwater River drainage area in 1860-1862 and the settlement that became Lewiston were on the Nez Perce Reservation, created in 1855, although the boundaries were not ratified by Congress. Trespass by whites without Nez Perce permission was forbidden by the treaty but, as the Indian agent at the time said, "trying to stop the miners was like trying to stop the wind." A new treaty forced on the Indians in 1863 reduced the reservation to one-sixth its original size, leaving out Lewiston and most of the mining area.

Chinese

Chinese poured into California in the 1850's and spread throughout the west following the shifting centers of excitement. Most Chinese were poorly treated by white Americans, many were persecuted, and more than a few were murdered. In many gold camps they became cooks and laundrymen. Many worked in gangs to build ditches and roads. Mining claims rules typically denied Orientals the right to own mining claims. Later, when claims began to play out and the whites wanted to sell out and move on to better diggings their sense of justice shifted remarkably and the Chinese were allowed to buy or lease such mine property. Some took over operation of claims that had been abandoned by whites. The Chinese were found to be good miners and generally continued working claims long after the white miners had left. Remaining from their labors are several Chinese walls, neat fences made of piled stones, near Granite, Union Creek, and elsewhere. Most of the towns had a "Chinatown" section, including Granite, Baker City, Sparta and Canyon City.

Several stories and legends of Chinese massacres exist. It is certain that unequal working conditions were a fact of life for Chinese laborers, but because of very little record keeping about working conditions for Chinese laborers, it is difficult to verify the accuracy of some of the accounts. Lily White Mine is often mentioned as a site of wrong doing perpetrated upon Chinese laborers, but Wallowa-Whitman National Forest Service research, including opening the old mine, has shown that story to be apochrophal. The other stories involved Chinese miners along the northern Snake River and Imnaha River. Those stories have, to a degree, been verified, that a number of Chinese miners camped along the river were apprently killed for their gold and supplies. Probably other incidents occurred. Certainly the newspapers of the time seemed to demonstrate a sharp prejudice against the Chinese.

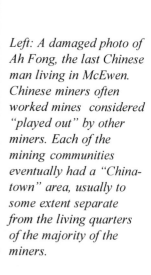

Left: A damaged photo of Ah Fong, the last Chinese man living in McEwen. Chinese miners often worked mines considered "played out" by other miners. Each of the mining communities eventually had a "Chinatown" area, usually to some extent separate from the living quarters of the majority of the miners.

Districts and Mines

Canyon City panorama, 1888. George Iriving Hazeltine, 1862 pioneer of Canyon City, a professional photographer in California before coming to Oregon. with back to camera (see also p. 46).

Canyon District

The Canyon District was the richest and, after Auburn, the second earliest, placer gold mining district in Northeastern Oregon. Estimates of placer mine production range as high as $26,000,000. Lode production was comparatively very small. Most of the gold deposits, both placer and lode, in the Canyon District are within a few miles of John Day, a small town at the junction of Canyon Creek and the John Day River. Canyon City is about a mile south up Canyon Creek from John Day. In this area the John Day River flows westward through a broad fertile valley bordered on the south by the high and rugged Strawberry Range. Canyon Creek flows northward through a steep-walled canyon cutting across the range. Elevations range from about 2,900 feet at Mount Vernon, 3,100 feet at John Day, 9,038 feet at the top of Strawberry Mountain, to 8,007 feet at the summit of Canyon Mountain.

Rocks exposed in the district are chiefly gabbro, peridotite, and serpentinite of the Canyon Mountain Complex. Greenstone and meta-argillite are exposed locally. The areas north of the river and the east side of Strawberry Mountain are covered by Tertiary basalt flows.Small cliffs of volcanic tuff and associated gravel of the Late Pliocene-Pleistocene Rattlesnake Formation are exposed along

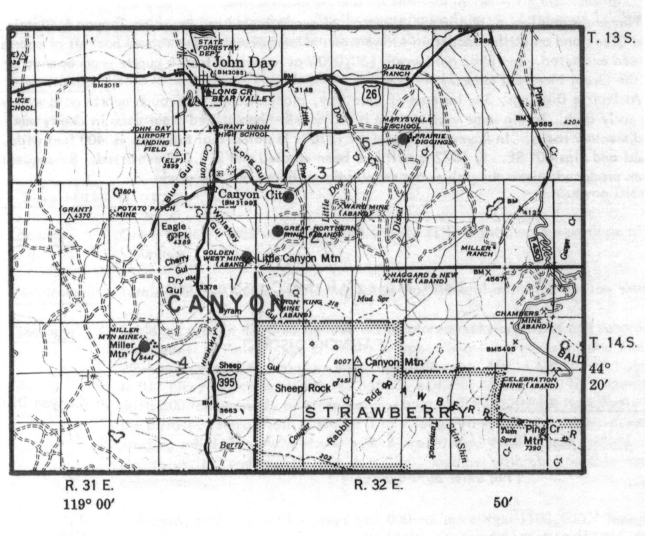

R. 31 E.
119° 00'

R. 32 E.

50'

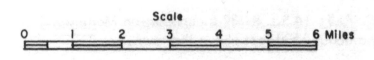

Scale

0 1 2 3 4 5 6 Miles

Base map from U.S. Forest Service

Lode Mines
1. Golden West
2. Great Northern
3. Haight
4. Miller Mountain
5. Prairie Diggings

Index Map of Gold Belt of the Canyon District

the highway east and west of John Day.

Gold was discovered in the gulch now known as Canyon Creek (Grant County) on June 8, 1862, by William C. Allred, who was with a group of 60 miners from California who were on their way to Florence, Idaho, one of several camps in western Idaho where rich gold placer deposits had recently been found. The rest of the group chose to ignore Allred's find and to continue to Florence. For his own safety Allred went along with them. When the group reached Auburn they were told that the Florence mines were petering out so Allred and 17 of his companions returned to the Canyon Creek discovery only to find the creek banks lined with miners panning and sluicing gold.

Within a year, newspapers of the time reported, 5,000 miners were working gravel along the creek and nearby areas. Grant County was carved from Wasco County and Canyon City was named and remains its county seat. Probably the population estimate given in the newspaper was somewhat exaggerated. In a letter to his wife dated August 17, 1862 (Rand, 1981), Irving Hazeltine estimated the population at about 1,000. In the same letter he said that supplies for John Day's River area came from The Dalles about 200 miles away via the The Dalles Military Road. He referred to the gulch as Whiskey Gulch. Lewis said 1,000 to 1,500 people were there in the winter of 1862-63. Canyon City townsite was laid out July 20, 1862, and John Day, about one mile north, was started shortly thereafter. Initially they were mostly tent towns. Some early buildings were crude shacks with canvas tops. Then came cabins made of logs and rough-sawed lumber. The first lumber was whipsawed and sold for $300 per thousand board feet. A little later a mill was established in Canyon City and lumber prices dropped significantly. Post Offices opened in April 1864 in Canyon City and in 1865 in John Day. Pack trains from the Dalles brought in groceries, whiskey, and tobacco. Saloons were among the first business establishments.

Homesteaders began arriving in the fall of 1862 hoping to make a living by farming and selling the farm products to the mining population. Lewis says, "The first families to arrive came from California in July, 1863….this train consisted of thirty two wagons, one hundred and five men, fourteen women and several children" (Lewis, 1962).

Like most mining towns, Canyon City and John Day had an abundance of saloons, gambling halls, dance halls and houses of ill repute. Canyon City had a Chinatown. Lewis reported that 500-600 Chinese may have lived there at one time.

During the 1860s the Chinese could not own real estate including mining claims, so they worked in the mines for wages, or worked abandoned claims. Some started small businesses such as laundries, small grocery stores, boarding houses, and delivery services.

Lewis reports that during the 1870s, Chinese companies secured control of many old creek claims that had not been thoroughly worked and scores of Chinese were employed in sifting the gravel in search of the golden metal. When Chinatown burned in 1885, the Chinese were not allowed to rebuild there so they moved to John Day" *(History of Baker, Grant, Malheur and Harney Counties, 1902, pp. 435 and 443).* Dennis Smith told me that Canyon City burned three different times: 1870, 1898, and 1937.

Canyon Creek and nearby streams, gulches, and hillsides proved to be the most productive of all the early-day placer districts in the Blue Mountains. Early output may have been as much as

54

*Columbus Sewel, a black man, worked as a drayman, raising a family in the Canyon City and John Day areas in the early days (mentioned in Hazeltine's letters in the book book,*Whiskey Gulch*). Helen Rand says that Sewel came to the area with Bradford C. Trowbridge during the early days of the gold rush. Trowbridge, Hazeltine and Billy Wilson pur-chased a piece of land bordering the present fair grounds. Trowbridge bought out Wilson and Hazeltine and with Sewel's help developed the Trowbridge Ranch the first ranch in Grant County. Sewel later raised a family who lived in the county all their lives.*

$26,000,000.   Lindgren says probably not over $15,000,000. Lewis says $20,000,000 was taken from the Canyon City and Marysville areas. He mentions pans containing $150 worth of gold. Annual output during the first few years was estimated at $3,000,000 to $5,000,000 (Lindgren). Output averaged $22,000 per week during 1865 or about $1,000,000 per year, but had fallen to $300,000 in 1870 (Raymond, 1870). For several succeeding years output remained at about $100,000 annually, then dwindled to a few thousand per year till 1916 when dredging started.

In 1882 there were 16 hydraulic plants (many of them small) in operation and two thirds of the products were from Chinese companies (Lindgren, 1901, p. 719). Part of the production came from the Humboldt Diggings, an excavation on the west wall of Canyon Creek that is about one mile long, several hundred feet wide and as much as 80 feet high. Located about 150 feet above the level of Canyon Creek, a caption on a photo of the Humbodt says, "Mine worked 20 years. Each year $15,000 to $17,000. Chinese labor employed." Lindgren said the Humboldt was worked over 30 years prior to his visit, production being between $10,000 and $20,000 per season. Humboldt mine went into receivership in 1911. Court records show who owned the mine at different times between 1882 and 1911. During most of those years ownership was an eight-way partnership. Ira Sproul was a consistent owner and was listed as manager in 1882. The court record also said that production of the mine appears to have stopped many years previous to 1911.

Lindgren (1901, p.719) said the bedrock is coarse, cemented gravel; the pay is said to be concentrated in the first 4 feet overlying the bedrock. The exposed bedrock is nearly level but is said to dip gently westward. Because the gold bearing alluvium is far less consolidated than the underlying gravel it is assumed to be considerably younger and to have been deposited by Canyon Creek.

Water to work the placers required ditches. Oliver (1936, p.24) said that the first ditch built by the Canyon Creek miners in 1862 was called the Rawhide Ditch because flumes were built of rawhide due to the lack of lumber. Lewis said The Humboldt Ditch was begun in 1862. It was named for the fact that its first owners were from Humboldt County, California. Water from this ditch was first used by hand placer miners along Canyon Creek, then later was used by hydraulic mines at higher elevations including the Humboldt Diggings.

The Kam Wah Chung and Co. Museum occupies the old stone building in the John Day City Park. Doc Ing Hay, a traditional Chinese herbal doctor, lived and worked there when it served as a general store, religious shrine, and opium den. Hay treated patients there from 1887 until he locked the door for the last time in 1948. Many of his goods, medicines, and supplies, including 500 containers of herbs, remain in the building (See *History of Baker, Grant, Malheur and Harney Counties*, 1902, pp. 435, 443). The area, including the building, is now a part of the Oregon State Park system.

A notable resident of Canyon City in the early days was Cinncinatus Hiner (Joaquin) Miller (1837-1913), who wore many hats during his long life: cowhand, horse thief, express rider, gold miner, cook, author, poet, journalist, news reporter and editor, county judge, among other pursuits. He moved to Canyon City in 1864, living there with a wife and child for about four years before moving on to broader horizons in 1868.

Herman Oliver (1961) devoted about three pages in his book to Miller saying he was Grant County's gift to literature and a famous figure in Europe and that before moving to Canyon City he spent time in northern California where he lived with Indians and married an Indian woman. Later he was editor of a newspaper in Eugene, Oregon. While there his pro-slavery writings outraged his readers and in 1862 a Federal Court closed his paper down. Meanwhile, he had left his Indian bride

Canyon City, ca. 1900-1910. Freight wagon on Washington Street.

and married Minnie Myrtle Dyer of Curry County. "Miller was Grant County's first elected county judge. He had little formal schooling but his head was bursting with wild poetic ideas about sun, waves, love, mountains steams, man and nature. He could be seen all up and down Canyon Creek, sometimes drunk and sometimes sober but always with a notebook." In 1868, two volumes of his poetry written in Canyon City were published by Carter and Himes in Portland. He later adopted the nickname Joaquin from the outlaw Joaquin Murieta, whom he admired, thinking it a better name for a poet than Cincinnatus.

Strawberry Mountain looking south.

Dredges later produced a minimum of 120,000 ounces of gold and 13,000 ounces of silver from gravel deposits along the John Day River above and below John Day extending from near John Day to Mount Vernon. Lode production records are scarce, involved probably 5,000-20,000 ounces of gold with low silver content.

Joaquin Miller's cabin in Canyon City.

Above: John Day, date unknown. Probably 1880-1900.
Below: Canyon City, ca. 1900, courtesy of Oregon Dept. of Geology and Mineral Industries.

Above: Humboldt Diggings. The streams of water shown working from four directions washed away large quanities of earth and changed the landscape.

Below: Caption typed on picture states, "This picture shows how it was done. Placer mining near Marysville about one mile east of Canyon City, about the years 1875-1880."

Above: Dredge operating between John Day and Canyon City, 1916-1917, near the site of the present Grant County High School. It was the second of two dredges built in the area.

Dredges in the Canyon District

In 1916 a bucketline dredge was installed by Empire Dredge Co. near the town of John Day. It operated almost continuously until it was dismantled and moved to Prairie City in 1929. The dredge produced about $1,750,000 in gold and silver (*Engineering and Mining Journal*, 1929, pp. 736-737).

A large dragline dredge owned by Ferris and Marchbank began work in the John Day River about 4 miles below John Day in 1935, and in 1937 a connected-bucket dredge was installed by Western Dredging Co. Both operations ceased in 1942. Recorded production from the Canyon District for the years 1935-1942 was $2,539,214, most of it from dredges.

Combined recorded output from dredge operations extending from Canyon City to John Day on Canyon Creek then up the John Day a mile or two then down the John Day nearly to Mount Vernon during 1916-1942 was 123,911 ounces gold and 13,066 ounces silver (DOGAMI Bulletin 61, 1968). Geology of the area includes small quartz veins with hematite and calcite in gabbro, ultramafic rocks, greenstone, meta-argillite, and graywacke.

Above and below: Placer mines near Dayville, Canyon District.

Right: Hydraulic placer on the John Day River, about one mile east of Canyon City. DOGAMI Bulletin 14B says a large area was hydraulicked in the heyday of early placer mining on the John Day River.

Marysville Area

Marysville, situated 1.5 miles east of Canyon City, is said by Lindgren (1901) to have produced a large amount of gold in early days from hand and hydraulic placers. How much of the millions of dollars produced in Canyon district came from Marysville placers is unknowable due to lack of records.

Lindgren (1901) says the rich gravels of Marysville and the gravels of the present drainages above Marysville are comparatively recent deposits. The gold is likely derived from the rich pocket veins of Canyon Mountain. Some of the gold bearing gravel deposits have been worked almost up to the veins.

Many shallow placer pits and ditches dot a gently sloping area that is several hundred acres in size. Average depth of mining appears to have been about 10 feet or less. Gravel ranges up to about 1 foot in diameter. Bedrock is serpentinite and altered gabbroic rocks.

Left:I. B.. Hazeltine with gold pan and Charles Schryer with hydraulic nozzel; placer near Marysville, 1900.

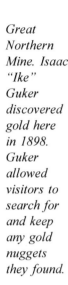

Great Northern Mine. Isaac "Ike" Guker discovered gold here in 1898. Guker allowed visitors to search for and keep any gold nuggets they found.

Great Northern Mine

The old Great Northern Mine is on the north side of Canyon Mountain about two miles southeast of Canyon City at about 4700 ft elevation, 1500 ft above the town. Parks and Swartley (1916, pp. 111-112). reported that the Great Northern and most other gold deposits on Canyon Mountain are not in well-defined quartz veins but in quartz–calcite seams "which are quite numerous everywhere."

In 1897, Isaac "Ike" Guker discovered a pocket of decomposed quartz through which ran innumerable golden wires. He took out $700 or $800 worth of gold in a few days and had "bushels" of such material left (from *History of Baker, Grant, Malheur and Harney Counties*). It is estimated that $67,000 worth of gold was taken out of the deposit. Guker reportedly let visitors search for and keep any nuggets they found (from Grant County pamphlet). DOGAMI Bulletin 14-B, 1941, p.25, says in 1898 a $30,000 pocket was extracted from one of the seams in a surface cut on this property. A few pockets of lesser importance were found later during extensive underground exploration.

Prairie Diggings

This property, about 3 miles east of Canyon City, was evidently mined extensively for placer gold in early days. Ground disturbance in the photo at right shows that a large acreage was involved. The *History of Baker, Grant, Malheur and Harney Counties* says the Prairie Diggings placer was first worked in 1862 by a party of 18 Germans including F. C. Sels, who later operated a brewery in Canyon City. The party located 18 claims and dug out $180,000, worth of placer gold, $10,000 apiece, the first year.

Placer mining uncovered a body of quartz veins intertwined with country rock 400 feet wide. In 1864, J. A. Laycock formed a corporation that built a 10-stamp mill and produced $26,000 worth of gold. Stockholder squabbles curtailed further production.

An article in the March 28, 1990, issue of *The Mining World* reported results of recent drilling, from 139 holes totalling 18,177 feet on the property by GSR Gold Search Resources. Assay results presented for parts of 8 holes ranged from 0.042 to 0.067 ounces gold per ton. Clyde Holliday told me (Aug. 2, 2004, by phone) that the Prairie Diggings prospect is on ranch land he and family acquired and have lived on since 1948. He said that in 1948 there was a stamp mill at Prairie Diggings and four or more houses at the mine. The mill was housed in a tall frame building built with wooden pins instead of nails. The Hollidays tore down the building and mill and built two large barns from the lumber. He doesn't remember the number of stamps in the mill but steel rods remain on the site. Holiday expressed his belief that the mine and mill produced very little gold but has no knowledge of how much placer gold was produced prior to his acquisition of the property.

The Miller Mountain Mine

According to the DOGAMI Bulletin 14-B, 1941, description "this was the most extensively developed lode gold deposit in the Canyon District. The aggregate length of three tunnels is about 4,000 feet and stoping on the steeply dipping vein extends for well over 500 feet in many places…." The main drift in the mine is about 800 feet long and from this drift there are 7 rises of ore. No records of production have been found.

Prairie Diggings, three miles east of Canyon City, a placer mine.

Two views of Canyon City ca. 1905. Match house in lower right above with same in lower left below.

Above: Street crowd observing a large sawed timber on wheels on Washington Street, Canyon City. Timbers that size possibly were destined for use in mine-mill construction..

Left: Austin Placer. Miners appear to be sluicing bedrock.

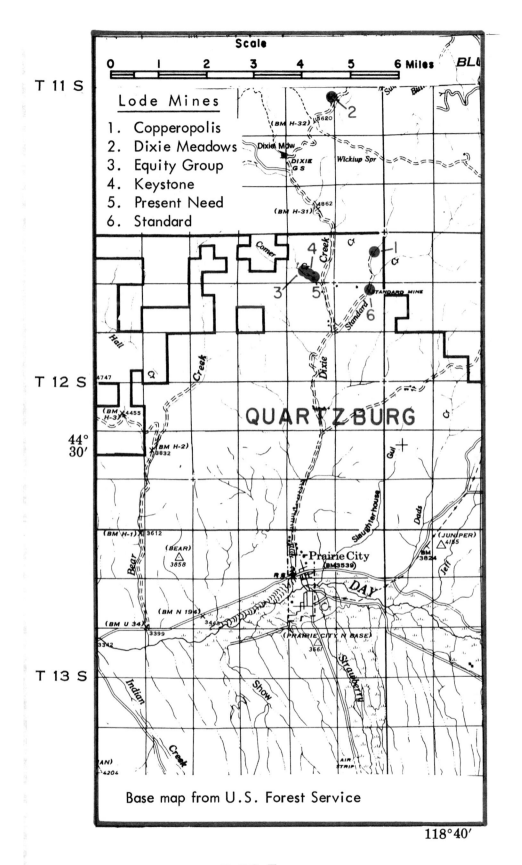

Index Map of Quartzburg District

Prairie City in the Quartzburg District. The town is at the junction of Dixie Creek and the John Day River. The first town in the Quartzburg district was Dixie, located about 5 miles up Dixie Creek from the John Day River. Residents moved to Prairie City as mining encroached on the town.

Quartzburg District

This district encompasses Prairie City and all of the Dixie Creek drainage including Standard Creek, plus a small area on the north side of the divide at the head of Ruby Creek. Dixie Creek flows southward into the John Day River at Prairie City. Ruby Creek flows north into the Middle Fork of the John Day River. The first town in the district was Dixie located about 3 miles up Dixie Creek from present Prairie City. It was started in 1862. A post office was established on August 8, 1862. Prairie City was so named for the prairie-like appearance of the land along the John Day River south and east of the town. The name Dixie honored southerners who were among the first miners. Lindgren (1901, p. 272) reported that placer mining, mostly on Dixie Creek, began in 1862 and the deposits were reported rich, though no production figures were available. Raymond (1870) said there were 100 white men and 200 Chinese employed in the Dixie Creek placers in 1869 and that in 1873 the creek was turned over to the Chinese. In 1882 two small hydraulic operations produced $30,000 worth of gold (Mint report via Lindgren, p. 272). The placers consisted of gravel accumulated in the creek bed to depths of 10 or 15 feet. The workings extend upstream from Prairie City for about five miles. The width of the gravel-covered river bottom is from 300 to 800 feet, the whole of which has been worked (Lindgren, 1901, p. 272). During 1930-1936 a bucket-line dredge owned by Empire Dredging Co. mined about a mile and a half of the John Day River below Prairie City. The H. D. England Company dragline dredge worked in Dixie Creek above Prairie City almost continuously between October 1938 and April 1941. The dredge was then moved to Trout Creek near Burns (Dogmi Bull. 14 B).

Brooks and others (1982) show the location of 63 Lode mines and prospects in the district, most of which have produced little or no gold. Dogami Bulletin 14-B briefly describes 32 mines and prospects in the district, of which Gilluly Reed and Park (1933) had described 18. Most of the lode mines are located more than six miles up Dixie Creek near and above the Standard Creek junction. Productive lode mines include the Equity, Dixie Meadows, Standard, and Keystone. Lode mine production records are scarce. The Equity Mine property was discovered and located in 1878 and was worked almost continuously until about 1910 producing between $400,000 and $600,000 in gold and silver. Combined ore shoots, 350 feet in combined length, were mined out above creek level long ago. The vein is mostly quartz with some carbonate and massive sulfides consisting of pyrite, chalcopyrite, galena, and sphalerite. A small amount of development work was done and about 45 tons of ore was produced in 1933-1940 (Dogami Bulletin 14-B, p. 114).

Development of the Dixie Meadows Mine, located near the head of Ruby Creek just beyond the Dixie Creek divide, was started in 1900 by Messers Kite and Reese. A mill was built in 1903 and by 1910 about 350 tons running $50.00 per ton had been shipped to a smelter. The mine had produced less than $100,000 by 1940. Beginning in 1973 Dixie Meadows Exploration Ltd., a Canadian firm, conducted an exploration program at the Dixie Meadows Mine including some diamond drilling. Two leach pads (50 feet by 100 feet) were built in order to test the amenability of the ores to heap-leach cyanidation. The company gave up their lease in the early 1980s. Company reports said the gold mineralization is associated with a shear zone 60 feet in average width and several thousand feet long. Rocks cut by the shear zone include greenstone, diorite, serpentinite, and argillite. Within the shear zone the rocks have been brecciated and partly replaced by quartz with some sericite, and sulfide minerals, including pyrite, arsenopyrite, chalcopyrite, pyrrhotite, galena, marcasite, and sphalerite.

The Standard Mine is on the Standard Creek fork of Dixie Creek about seven miles from Prairie City. The Standard vein, ranging from a few inches to 4 feet in width, has been developed by over 3700 ft of workings from three adits at vertical intervals of 80 feet and a 70 foot vertical shaft. Vhay (1960) estimated that about 10,000 tons of ore had been removed from stopes in the Standard Mine prior to 1960. This mine produced copper, gold, and a very small amount of cobalt. Incomplete records indicate that about 1,401 ounces of gold and 224,741 pounds of copper were produced from 8,256 tons of ore during the periods 1906-1907 and 1964-1965 (Brooks and others, 1984). Small amounts of cobalt and gold-bearing ore were shipped to Europe and to the Edison Laboratories in New York for test purposes. In the 1960s several truck loads of hand sorted ore were shipped to the Tacoma smelter, 57 tons of which averaged 0.5 ounce gold, 1.2 ounces silver, and 20 percent copper.

Goldbug Mine, Quartzburg District.

Copperopolis Mill. About 250 tons of ore was milled prior to 1906.

The photo is stamped "Susanville, Oregon." Susanville is a good example of the way towns sprang up wherever gold was found, in the bottoms of gulches, as in this case, or on the steep sides or tops of mountains. This photo is a contrast of black and white due to snow.

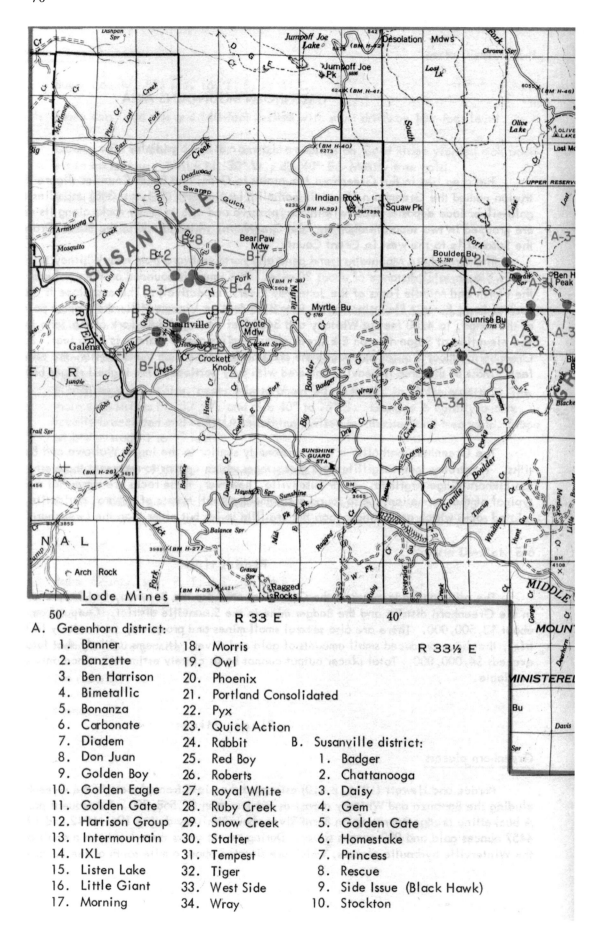

Lode Mines

A. Greenhorn district:

1. Banner
2. Banzette
3. Ben Harrison
4. Bimetallic
5. Bonanza
6. Carbonate
7. Diadem
8. Don Juan
9. Golden Boy
10. Golden Eagle
11. Golden Gate
12. Harrison Group
13. Intermountain
14. IXL
15. Listen Lake
16. Little Giant
17. Morning

18. Morris
19. Owl
20. Phoenix
21. Portland Consolidated
22. Pyx
23. Quick Action
24. Rabbit
25. Red Boy
26. Roberts
27. Royal White
28. Ruby Creek
29. Snow Creek
30. Stalter
31. Tempest
32. Tiger
33. West Side
34. Wray

B. Susanville district:

1. Badger
2. Chattanooga
3. Daisy
4. Gem
5. Golden Gate
6. Homestake
7. Princess
8. Rescue
9. Side Issue (Black Hawk)
10. Stockton

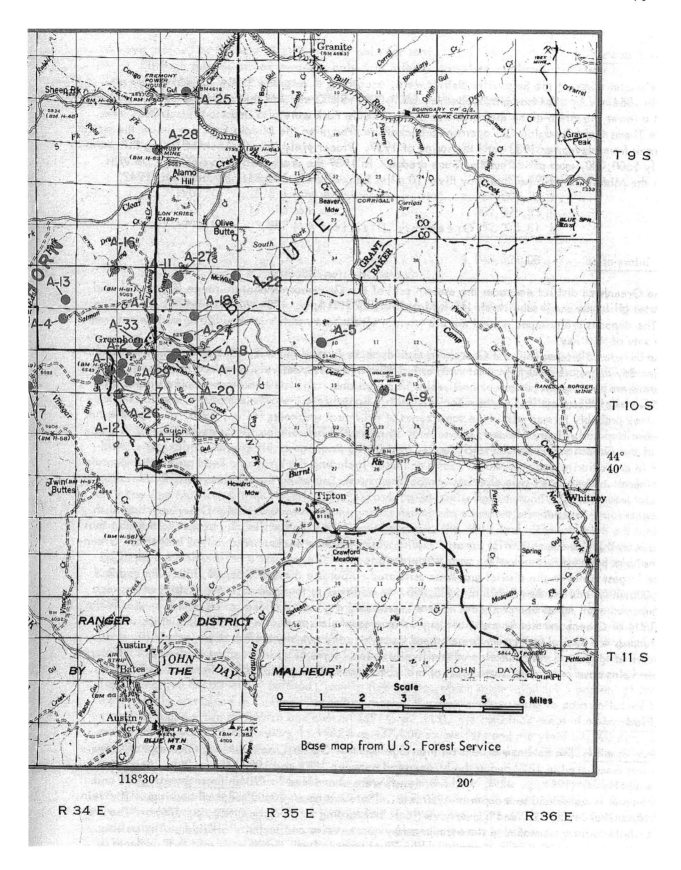

Map of Greenhorn and Susanville Districts

Susanville District

Susanville District is about 22 miles down the Middle Fork of the John Day River from Austin Junction where Highways 7 and 26 meet. Remnants of the town are on Elk Creek about a mile up stream, east of the river. Galena, situated on the bank of the river just below the mouth of Elk Creek grew apace with Susanville. Both had post offices. The Susanville placers were discovered in 1864 and were worked practically every season prior to 1914. Total production to that time was estimated at $600,000. The mines are all on the north side of the river. Elk Creek has been the largest producer, but Deep Creek, one mile below Susanville, as well as Onion Creek and Big Creek farther down the river, yielded considerable placer gold.

The Buck Gulch placer, located about 3 miles north of Galena and about a thousand feet above the river, was noted for yielding some large gold nuggets, one of which was the Armstrong Nugget found by George Armstrong on June 19, 1913, where he and his son were placer mining on claims they owned. The nugget, on display at the U. S. National Bank in Baker City, weighs 80.4 ounces troy and was valued at $17.60 per ounce or $1415 at that time. At today's gold price ($600 per ounce) the gold would be worth about $45,240. The nugget was 85 percent pure gold

Later, the Timms Gold Dredging Co. operated a bucketline dredge on the Middle Fork of the John Day River just below the mouth of Elk Creek from November 1933 until the Spring of 1939. Placer production from the district during that time period was nearly $500,000 most of it from the dredge. In 1939, the dredge was moved to the DeWitt ranch on the Middle Fork of the John Day River 10 miles below Bates.

Rocks exposed in the district are mainly quartz-rich schists with some slate, quartzite, greenstone, serpentinized peridotite, and gabbro all of which are cut by silicic dikes. The dikes probably are related to the quartz diorite intrusive exposed along the northern and western parts of the district.

Lode gold deposits were found in quartz veins and replacement bodies in schist. Many of the veins filled fissures paralleling the schistocity. The deposits are in a narrow belt 2 miles wide by 4 miles long extending northeast from Galena.

Placer on Elk Creek, Susanville District.

Lode gold production estimates range between $250,000 and $500,000 most of it from the Badger Mine between 1899 and 1905. Development of the Badger Mine includes a 900-foot shaft, a 1600-foot crosscut adit on the 500-foot level and several hundred feet of drifts. The ore contained between 8% and 11% recoverable sulfide minerals. Total recovery was between 58% and 60% of the assay value. Two veins were productive. They are six feet apart and vary from 1 to 20 feet thick.

Greenhorn District

Greenhorn is the highest and smallest incorporated ghost town in Oregon. The town is located about 60 miles west of Baker City via Oregon Highway 7 and a good graveled road. The mining district extends from Greenhorn west to include Vinegar Hill, Sunrise Butte, and Ben Harrison Peak. Old mines in that area include the Ben Harrison, Morris, and Tiger. Rocks exposed include quartz diorite of the Sunrise Butte stock and a mix of serpentinite, argillite, gabbro, and greenstone which pre-date the stock. Mines to the east of Greenhorn include the Bonanza Mine and the Geiser Creek and Winterville placers.

Lilliland indicates that the first settlement in the region was Robinsonville, established in 1865. It burned in 1898. The first Greenhorn townsite near the Robinsonville site burned in 1900. A second, the present Greenhorn, was built about 0.7 mile southwest of Robinsonville. It started as a tent town. The first wooden building was a saloon. Patent to the 53.58 acre townsite was issued in 1912 to then mayor Simeon C. Richardson, who states, "During its boom days, 1910-1915, the city of Greenhorn housed two hotels, a post office, waterworks including fire hydrants, a number of general merchandise and grocery stores, several saloons, one house of prostitution, and later a wooden jail."

The mines are clustered near the eastern end of the granitic intrusive body that some call the Greenhorn batholith. Ferns and others (1983) show the locations of 84 mines and prospects on their geologic map of the Greenhorn quadrangle; Brooks and others (1984) show 72 such localities on their map of the adjoining northeast quarter of the Bates quadrangle. Most of the deposits have produced little or no gold. The deposits occur in a wide variety of rock types. The Bonanza, Red Boy, and Pyx mines are in argillite.

Within a circle four miles across around Greenhorn there are a multitude of small mines and prospects in apparently near-surface veins in metagabbro, metadiorite, and serpentine. Fragmentary records suggest that these mines have produced about $200,000 in gold. These small producers include the Don Juan, IXL, Bi-metallic, and Rabbit. Extensive exploration at several mines revealed that the veins are non-persisitent in length and depth.

The bulk of lode mine production has come from the Bonanza, Red Boy, Ben Harrison, and Pyx mines. Estimated yield from early day placers in the Greenhorn District, including Bonanza and Whitney areas, is at least $1,568,000 (Pardee and Hewett, 1914).

Parts of Burnt River in Whitney Valley have been dredged. This district includes also the Winterville, Parkerville, McNamee Gulch, and Geiser Creek placers east of Greenhorn. The Triangle Dredge worked about a mile and one half of channel gravels along Slab Creek and the North Fork of Burnt River about two miles southeast of Greenhorn.(DOGAMI file). Timms Dredge worked on the Middle Fork of Burnt River.

The lode gold deposits were in quartz veins in argillite, granodiorite, greenstone, and altered mafic to ultramafic intrusive rocks. Deposits occur near the edges of the Greenhorn batholith. Many of the veins are associated with porphyritic granitic dikes.

Above: Four miners in front of a cabin or possibly the mess hall at the Intermountain Mine, Greenhorn District.
Below: Greenhorn Main Street following a snow storm.

Left: The Ben Harrison Store, Greenhorn.

Right: Snow Creek Mine, Greenhorn District.

Psyche Mine.

Above: Psyche Mine, Greenhorn District.

Left: Ben Harrison Mine, Greenhorn District. A miner is transferring broken ore from an ore chute to an ore car for hauling out of the mine

Transporting supplies and equipment was an essential part of daily life for early miners. Above, hauling a boiler from the railroad at Sumpter to the Bonanza Mine required many teams of horses. Below, a multi-team hitch transporting a ratchet wheel for the shaft hoist at Red Boy Mine.

Above: Greenhorn, Main Street, 1913.
Below: Hay wagon on Greenhorn's Main Street, driven by Jim
Brennon, bound for the Bi-Metalic Mine about 1914, according
to Brooks Hawley.

Bonanza Mine

The 1902 *History of Baker, Grant, Malheur, and Harney Counties* says that the Bonanza vein was discovered in 1877 by a pioneer prospector named Jack Hazard (Lindgren says Jack Haggard), who sold it in 1879 for $350 to the Bonanza Mining Company. The mine was worked for ten years by the original locators using an arrastra for ore reduction. In 1885, Portland capitalists purchased the mine, erected a ten-stamp mill, and operated for two years with little success. In 1891, the Geiser family obtained part of the mine property as payment of a $2,000 debt and paid $3,000 for the balance of the property. They re-opened old workings and operated the mine and mill continuously from 1892 to approximately 1907.

The Bonanza Mine is about four air miles airline nearly due east of Greenhorn near the head of Geiser Creek. The 1899-1904 production by the Geiser Company was $904,624. The value per ton of ore milled averaged $17.85. The vein, averaging 5 or 6 feet in width, is developed to a depth of 1,250 ft. Under-ground workings total 18,000 ft. including several adits and a shaft. The production before 1892 was inconsiderable though extending over a series of years (Lindgren). The Geiser family reportedly took out several hundred thousand dollars then sold the mine. When they sold the mine, ore reserves worth $300,000 were believed to be in sight. After1898, that or a greater amount of gold was extracted, making the total production well up toward the million-dollar mark, according to Pardee and Hewett (p.119). After its purchase for $500,000 by the Consolidated Bonanza Gold Mines Company, a Pittsburgh, Pennsylvania corporation, the mine was vigorously exploited until December 1904, when the pumps were drawn and the workings below the adit level were allowed to fill with water. The mine has been operated from time to time since that date, ore being drawn from the upper older workings, but at present only part of these are accessible. Total production has been about $1,750,000 (Parks and Swartley, p. 39).

The following record of 1899-1904 production is from Pardee and Hewett (1914, p. 120).

1899		$ 146,419.47 a
1900		175,953.45 a
1901	14,885 tons ore	279,556.42 b
1902	5,371 tons ore	4,003.08 b
1903	11,495 tons ore	202,375.85 b
1904	3,887 ton ore	52,315.81 b
		_____
		$ 904,624.08

a. probably; b. gross

Gross recovery from the 35,638 tons of ore produced during 1901-1904 was $636,251; value per ton averaged $17.85. The vein is developed to a depth of 1,250 ft. Underground workings total 18,000 feet including several adits and a shaft.

The vein is composed of quartz cemented argillite breccia cut by numerous quartz veinlets of various sizes. It strikes N 55 E and is nearly vertical. Ore shoots averaged 5 to 6 ft. but in places swelled to 40 feet wide. The gold was about 600 fine and about 70 percent free-milling in upper levels. Sulfide content reportedly increased somewhat with depth. Concentrates varied from $20 to $60 per ton. The ore is believed to have averaged $7 to $12 per ton in value, but lenses of ore 8 to 16 inches wide were mined which ran as high as $1,400 per ton, and several hundred tons are said to have yielded an average of $100 in free gold per ton.

Bonanza Mine camp (called Geiser).

Bonanza Mill

George Cross News Letter (744 West Hastings St.,Suite 114 Vancouver 1, B.C.) dated November 29, 1974, carried the following: "Tapin Copper Mines, Ltd. recently reported that the No. 1 diamond drill hole on its Bonanza gold property, located 50 miles west of Baker City, Oregon, averaged 70 feet of

Right: Underground drilling, Bluebird Mine, Red Boy District. Miners are drilling blast holes in rock containing white streaks that probably are quartz veins containing some gold.

Left: Bluebird Mill, Red Boy District.

1.79 ounces gold per ton. Tapin stock rose from 60 cents a share to $3.55 on the news of the strike and the Vancouver stock exchange was forced to halt trading briefly because there was not enough stock on the market to meet the demand." Later, according to an *Oregonian* article on January 29, 1975, a group of minority stock holders filed suit claiming they were misinformed about the strike, since a redrilling of the core samples a week later produced only traces of gold and silver. The company claimed the redrilling produced cores with poor recovery and was too far from the original hole to produce meaningful comparison.

The Vancouver stock exchange ordered the company to turn over the non-assayed portion of the original cores, but those samples turned up stolen, according to an account in the <u>Vancouver Sun</u>. Following these events the Securities Commission of British Columbia froze "certain of the assets" of Tapin pending resolution of the case.

Geiser Grand Hotel

The Geiser family used part of the money from the Bonanza mine to buy and add improvements to the Warshauer Hotel in Baker City. The name was changed to Geiser Grand Hotel and it was long afterward known as the finest luxury hotel between Seattle and Salt Lake City. After being closed for several decades the hotel has recently been completely renovated (total cost: about $7,000,000 or more than 100 times its original cost) and reopened for business in 1995.

Red Boy Mine

The Red Boy Mine is near the head of Congo Gulch, a tributary of Clear Creek, about 5 mile southwest of Granite. The Red Boy was operated between 1890 and 1914 producing about $1,000,000 in gold and silver. Lindgren (p. 80) says, "Two mills were erected on the property, each failing to achieve success. After that Messrs A. J. Godfrey and Clark Taber, the present owners, built a small Crawford Mill,

Assay office at Red Boy Mine.

which did excellent work for some time. Finally in October, 1898 the present 20 stamp mill was installed which has run uninterruptedly and successfully until the present time " (p. 80). There was a cyanide plant at the mine.

The veins are fault zones five to seven feet wide (Lindgren says 3 to 15 feet wide) consisting of crushed argillite and, locally, softened porphyritic rock in which the broken rock is cemented by a great number of quartz seams.

An excessive amount of water in the lower levels made mining difficult and expensive. Presently, stone cribbing in the hillside marks the location of one of the mill buildings. Bonnie Skidgel (*Oregon Trail Traveler*, May 19, 1992) says: "Nearly $1 million in gold and silver bullion was produced between 1886 and 1912....Half of the value was from about 70,000 tons of ore mined between 1898 and 1902 by Clark Taber and A. J. Godfrey."

The Fremont Power Plant was built to furnish power to the Red Boy and other mines in the district and later produced power for public use. A dam was built to raise the level of Olive Lake five miles from the plant. Water to turn the turbines was carried to the plant in a 2-foot diameter wooden stave pipeline. The plant began producing power in 1908. *Baker Herald* (7-19-2001) reported that the Fremont Power Plant was acquired by the Eastern Oregon Light and Power Company in 1911 and by the California Pacific Utilities Company in 1940. The power plant was closed permanently in 1967. In 1968 California Pacific Utilities Company deeded the property to the U. S. Forest Service. Joe Batty and wife Sharon were caretakers at the powerhouse from 1968 to 1981. It remained a tourist attraction, drawing as many as 5,000 visitors one summer. The building's roof collapsed in 1993. A crew of National Guardsmen rebuilt much of the 2,300 square foot building in summer 1999. It was re-dedicated July 24, 2001. Oregon State Historic Preservation Office bestowed an award for the reconstruction. Umatilla National Forest now owns the building.

Red Boy Mine, Red Boy District.

Left: Red Boy cyanide plant

Below: stamps and amalgamation tables in Red Boy mill.

Pyx Mine

Pyx Mine is located about 2.7 miles across country northeast of Greenhorn. It produced a small amount of gold prior to 1900 and during 1907-1911. Ferns *et al.* said maybe $300,000. A 25-ton mill was installed in 1954. Myron Woodley began operating the mine in 1980 and by the end of 1989 he and a four-man crew had produced roughly $700,000 in gold. Mining was done during summer months only because roads into the Greenhorn area were closed by snow in winter. The gold was in a narrow quartz vein containing a little pyrite. The ore was trucked to Sumpter and treated in a small gravity and amalgamation mill. Much of the ore was high grade, consisting of coarse gold in white quartz.

Other mines in the Greenhorn District include the Snow Creek Mine and the Morning Mine (Brooks and Ramp p. 108). The Snow Creek Mine is said to have produced about $52,000 in gold and silver between 1902 and 1905. Some very small shipments were made in 1925-1927 and in 1939. Total production of the mine was probably more than $60,000. The vein in argillite and serpentine averages about 2 feet in width and strikes east. The mine is developed by a 240-foot shaft and a connecting crosscut adit 1,400 feet long. At the Morning Mine the most-developed vein lies along the footwall of a porphyritic diorite dike. This vein varies from 1 to 4 feet wide. Other smaller veins parallel or intersect the dike. Bill Gardener operated the mine and shipped some ore or concentrates to a smelter in the mid 1900s but production records are not available.

Concord Mine portal and crew. Red Boy District.

Cowden Glass Negatives

James Cowden, photographer, resided for a period of time in Sumpter, where he specialized in mine photos chiefly from the area within twenty to thirty miles of Sumpter. Ninety-two of Cowden's glass plate negatives are stored at Oregon Trail Regional Museum, which is also called Baker County Museum. A sampler of Cowden photos follow on this and the next four pages.

Right: Red Boy Mine prospect shaft.

In his photo collection, Brooks Hawley, a lifetime Sumpter resident, wrote the following about J. W. Cowden: "The J. W. Cowden photos from 8 x 10 glass plates of Sumpter and the surrounding mines in the period from about 1900 to 1906 are of considerable interest now although they had little attention in the intervening 50 or more years.

"It is hard to get much a story on them. Roscoe Deane remembered of J. W. Cowden that he was dignified person, 'always well dressed, wore a frock coat, was married, but had no children, only knew him to do photography and keep a rooming house, the J. W. Cowden, but I have not seen it.'

"An item in a *Blue Mountain American* states that J. W. Cowden was born in Troy, Missouri, in 1851, came to Sumpter in 1899, and was a millwright. An item in September, 1906 says that he had lately been in Nevada and was now returned to Sumpter. Likely he left Sumpter again soon after that and never came back. It is not known that he did any work as a millwright here but it could explain his interest in so often taking pictures of mine buildings. He no doubt made the pictures for sale but he did not seem to have a studio or to take portraits. He surely did his own developing and printing. He had a large house on the north side of North Street between Mill and Columbia Streets that shows in an old picture. It was used as a rooming house. Some teachers stayed there, as Professor Yoder. Cowden's house was acquired by Hatleys and later torn down. Perhaps they got their Cowden pictures from being left in the house. Grandma Hatley gave those pictures to Kenneth Alexander before she died and in July, 1963, Kenneth let me keep them after he had left them in my custody awhile. Those are all old prints and not negatives, about 52 and 4 not likely Cowden's, but not half of them of much interest.

"It would seem that when J. W. Cowden left Sumpter that he abandoned his camera and everything that went with it."

Snow Creek Mine, Greenhorn District.

Cowden photos, cont.

Fremont Power Plant pipeline construction at Ruby Camp.

Fremont Power Plant inside, ca. 1902.

Cowden photos, cont.

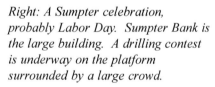

Left: Sumpter's Granite Street, ca. 1900.

Right: A Sumpter celebration, probably Labor Day. Sumpter Bank is the large building. A drilling contest is underway on the platform surrounded by a large crowd.

Left: Sumpter smelter. Writing on photo says, "Sumpter Smelter of the O. S. & R. Co."

Cowden photos, cont.

Sumpter Light and Power flume under construction.

Austin Station, which served as a stage station, a Sumpter Valley Railway station, a boarding house, and a restaurant.

Elkhorn Ridge Area
From west to east, Granite, Cable Cove, Cracker Creek, Sumpter, and Rock Creek Districts

These districts encompass the largest concentration of productive gold mines and prospects in northeast Oregon. At least 25 lode mines and prospects have been productive. Geologic quadrangle maps of the Granite (Brooks and others, 1982), Mount Ireland (Ferns and others, 1982), Bourne (Brooks and others 1982), and Elkhorn Peak (Ferns and others, 1987) show the locations of dozens of small mines and prospects, most of which have produced little or no gold. The lode gold deposits formed in quartz-rich veins and fracture zones in argillite and granodiorite intrusive rocks along the southern and western edges of the Bald Mountain batholith.

The most productive lode mines were the Buffalo Mine in the Granite District, five mines along the North Pole-Columbia Lode near Bourne in the Cracker Creek District, and the Baisley-Elkhorn and Highland-Maxwell mines in the Rock Creek District. Fragmentary records and estimates by early reporters indicate that total output from lode mines exceeds 650,000 ounces of gold and 1,500,000 ounces of silver. Mines along the North Pole Columbia Lode near Bourne, six miles north of Sumpter, produced about $8,000,000 in gold and silver during 1894-1916. The productive mines were the North Pole, Eureka and Excelcior (E and E), Taber Fraction, Columbia, and Golconda. The lode varies from 10 to 300 feet wide, has a productive strike length of 12,000 feet, and is traceable for 4 1\2 miles (Brooks and others). Bald Mountain, Ibex, Mammoth, and Belle of Baker are small mines which worked a vein about two miles west of the North Pole-Columbia Lode. Parts of this vein near Bald Mountain and Ibex mines were extensively explored in recent years.

Placer production began in 1862 and probably exceeds 550,000 ounces of gold. Dredging in Sumpter Valley during 1913-1924 and 1935-1954 produced more than 325,000 ounces of gold and 80,000 ounces of silver. Dredging in Granite District also produced large amounts of gold.

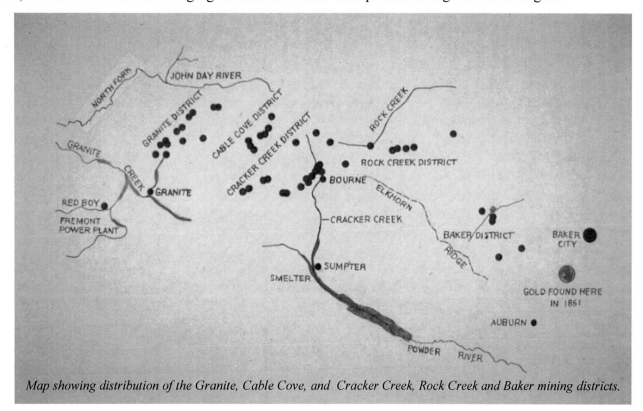

Map showing distribution of the Granite, Cable Cove, and Cracker Creek, Rock Creek and Baker mining districts.

Granite District

Granite District lies in the upper reaches of the North Fork of the John Day River that drain the west flank of the Elkhorn Mountains. The southern part of this area is drained by Granite Creek, Clear Creek, and Bull Run Creek and the northern part by Crane Creek and Onion Creek and the upper main stem of the North Fork of the John Day River. The old ghost town of Granite, one of the earliest settlements in eastern Oregon, is about 15 miles west of Sumpter via the Elkhorn Drive Scenic Byway. Timber is abundant. Elevations range from 4,683 at Granite to 7,000 feet at the La Belleview mine. The principal lode mines are in a northeast-trending belt about 2 miles wide and 5 mile long that extends from Cougar Mine on the southwest to La Belleview Mine on the northeast. The lode mines of Granite District lie along the southwestern edge of the Bald Mountain Batholith. The veins are mainly in older argillite of the Elkhorn Ridge argillite, but a few also cut granodiorite of the batholith. Dikes related to the batholith have been observed in several of the mines.

Gold was discovered on Granite Creek on Independence Day, July 4, 1862, by a group of prospectors from California on their way to gold camps in Idaho. Tabor (1988) says there were 50 men in the group led by his father, A. G. Tabor, and that he, J. W., was the first white child born in Grant County, Oregon, the latter date being December 31, 1865. It is hard to believe this; there were thousands of people in Grant County by then. Some members of the group went on to Idaho. Some stayed to investigate the new discovery and were quickly joined by other groups, many additional California miners, looking for new diggings. By September, 1862, the mines extended up Granite Creek for about eight miles from its mouth and reportedly were paying well. Flour sold for $35 for 100 pounds; bacon, $45; shovels, $4.50; axes, $6 (*Mining and Scientific Press*, 1862, via Priscilla Wegars, 1995, p. 35). A new town called Independence was started on Granite Creek about a half mile west of where the ghost town of Granite is located. About 1867 the town began moving slowly up-slope to the present site. Application for a Post Office in 1874 was denied because there was already a town in western Oregon named Independence. The name was changed to Granite and mail service was started.

By-laws adopted by the white miners in 1862 denied Chinese the right to own mining claims, but county records show that by 1867 Chinese individuals and companies had begun to purchase or lease mining claims in the district and some were reworking abandoned claims (Grant County Mining Records 1866-1881). The first time Chinese were allowed to own or lease and operate placer mines coincided with the lowering of water rates in the spring of 1865, as the yield of placer mines was diminishing and many white mine owners were moving on. Sales of mine property typically included all flume boxes, sluice boxes, tools, shovels, picks, crowbars, quicksilver, water rights, and cabins belonging to the claims; one purchase required payments in "Granite Creek gold dust." Claims sold varied considerably in size (Grant County Mining Records 1866-1881 via Priscilla Wegars, 1995, p.35).

Raymond (1870, p. 224) said there were about 40 Caucasians and 200 Chinese in Granite Creek Mining District in 1869. The 1870 Federal census for Granite precinct numbered 365 Chinese, all men; 337 were miners; and 83 were non-Chinese individuals. The number of Chinese dwindled to 132 in 1880, 13 in 1900, and none in 1910. Census records for 1890 were destroyed in a fire.

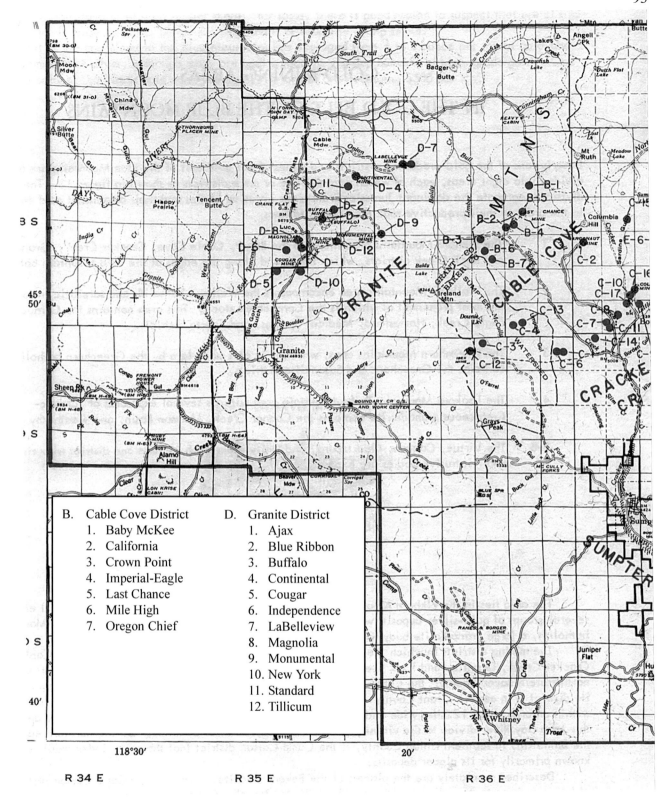

B. Cable Cove District
1. Baby McKee
2. California
3. Crown Point
4. Imperial-Eagle
5. Last Chance
6. Mile High
7. Oregon Chief

D. Granite District
1. Ajax
2. Blue Ribbon
3. Buffalo
4. Continental
5. Cougar
6. Independence
7. LaBelleview
8. Magnolia
9. Monumental
10. New York
11. Standard
12. Tillicum

**Index Map of Granite District with Cable Cove
and the west edge of Cracker District**

Granite, two views, left: looking east, Chinese occupied lower two rows of buildings.

Below: looking west. Largest building is the Granite Grand Hotel. The remnants of the older town of Independence by the creek near the center of the photo.

Granite Grand Hotel, 1895.

The Chinese proved to be good miners and continued working claims long after the white miners had left. Their legacy is a 60-acre site comprised of hand-stacked rock tailings on Granite Creek about a mile north of Granite known today as the "Chinese Walls" or the Ah Hee Diggings, a testimonial to many years of hard, persistent labor by dedicated people. The rocks were moved and stacked to get them out of the way of mining-associated gold bearing gravel, sand, and silt. A report on archaeological investigations of the site was published recently by Pricilla Wegars(1995). Steeves (1984) says the wall site is 750 yards long, parallel to the creek and 300 yards wide.

Whites returned to Granite during the lode-mining boom of 1890-1910 that affected other mine towns in northeastern Oregon such as Sumpter, Bourne, and Cornucopia. Census for the Granite precinct listed 836 nonwhites in 1900 and 148 in 1910.

The following is quoted from a 1910 Oregon Railroad and Navigation Company brochure entitled "Gold Fields of Eastern Oregon":

"The young camp of Granite has risen from nothingness to rustling, incorporated cityhood. like a mushroom in a night. A few weeks ago, it was rural crossroads. Now, it has a mayor and city council, six hotels and restaurants—one of the hotels having 65 rooms and another 25; — stores carrying from $15,000 to $25,000 stocks, two wide-awake newspapers, *The Boulder* and *The Gem*; four saloons, four livery, grain and feed establishments, drug-stores, blacksmith and carpenter shops and a gravity water system, affording protection from fire. Among the improvements contemplated or in course of construction are a $2,000 sawmill, an electric light and power plant, two churches, a public school, and a cold-storage plant. There are 12 producing mines immediately around the town, including the famous Red Boy, the May Queen, Cougar, Magnolia Ajax, Quebec, Polar Star, Bellevue, Inter-Mountain, Tempest, Buffalo and Intrinsic. There are 2,122 mining locations recorded in the Granite district, and many of them give every promise of becoming producers. Hundreds of tons of machinery are going in to the Granite mines and Baker and Grant counties are now spending $6,000 in improving the road between Sumpter and the new town. Surveys for the Granite-Hilgard railway have been made, and depot grounds at Granite have been granted and accepted. New and promising mines are constantly being discovered all over the region and the town bids fair to become an important center of golden activity."

The proposed Granite-Hilgard railway was never built.

The landmark Grand Hotel was built in mid-town Granite by Grant Thornburg and opened for business in 1893. It was sold to B. W. Levens in 1899 and a third story was added in December of that year. The hotel had 30 rooms. An annex attached later added 20 more rooms. The hotel was still standing but appeared abandoned and badly in need of repair and painting in a 1941 photograph in Tabor's "Granite and Gold." Tabor says the building was razed about 1943.

Above: Abandoned buildings in Granite. Photo taken about 1970.

Left: Sled load of ore concentrates from Buffalo Mine in front of a store in Granite, ca. 1960, enroute to Sumpter by sled, then on to the smelter by truck.

Gold production of the Granite District came mainly from placer deposits in the beds of three drainages: Granite, Bull Run, and Clear creeks and the Buffalo, Cougar-Independence, and La Belleview lode mines. The creeks named had produced a minimum of $1,033,000 in gold by 1914 (Pardee and Hewett, 1914). During 1938-1942 and 1946-1951 Porter Brothers Dredging Co. operated a bucketline dredge almost continuously on Granite, Bull Run, and Clear Creeks. Production from early day placer operations along the North Fork of the John Day River has been estimated at $893,000 prior to 1914 (Pardee and Hewett, 1914). The important mines of that era included the Klopp Mine and adjacent diggings near the mouth of Trail Creek, the French Diggings about six miles up the south fork of Trail Creek from the Klopp Mine, and the Thornburg placer on the North Fork about five miles below the Klopp. The deposits were worked mainly with hydraulic equipment.

Above: Buffalo Mine flotation mill with twenty-five tons daily capacity.

Below: Inside mill, Jim Jackson, mine operator, and Brooks Hawley discussing function of flotation cells in separating gold and gold-bearing minerals from waste material.

Small scale hand-placer mining along the North Fork and its tributaries has continued to the present day. The Davis and the Calhoun and Howell placers several miles farther down the North Fork were worked separately by washing plants and draglines during 1940-1942 and 1947-1950. Several thousand ounces of gold were produced.

Approximately three miles of river were worked prior to WWII by the Davis dragline dredge. The Calhoun and Howell dragline dredge worked up stream to the Big Creek junction in the years 1947-1950 and produced an estimated $200,000.

French Diggings

The French Diggings were located in Sections 20 and 29, T. 7 S., R. 36 E, several hundred acres in a compact area that extends from the summit of the divide at 6,800 feet elevation between North Fork of the John Day River and Trail Creek down to the latter stream at a point about 6 miles above its mouth and at an elevation of 6,000 feet.

Production estimates from different sources range from $387,000 to $1,000,000 (Parks and Swartley, 1916, p. 97). Tabor (1988) says his father discovered the deposits. Lawrence Neault (unpublished manuscript in DOGAMI mine files) says a group of Frenchmen, including ancestors of his, found the deposits and worked them for many years. DOGAMI Bulletin 14-B, 1941, p. 101 says discovery of the upper part of the property was made by two Frenchmen named Thibadeau and Nadeau. The lower claims were located by Dr. Louis Marrotte and Dr. A. Marrotte.

Buffalo Mine

The Buffalo Mine, also known as the Buffalo-Monitor Mine, was the longest operated lode gold mine in the Blue Mountains region. Mining began in the mid-1880s. Recorded 1903 through 1964 production was 33,418 ounces of gold and 239,305 ounces of silver from 42,246 tons of ore. No records are available for pre-1903 production. James Jackson who operated the mine during 1951-1965 suggested that considering the total area from which ore has been removed by stoping, the actual production may be about twice the recorded amount. The Buffalo Mine is developed by about 10,000

Buffalo Mine mucking machine. Brooks Hawley (left) visiting with James Jackson.

Entertaining visitors in front of the Jacksons' home and mine boarding house at the Buffalo Mine.

feet of drifts and crosscuts from four adit levels within a vertical range of 450 feet. The mine worked four roughly parallel quartz veins ranging from 1 to 6 feet thick and from 80 to 220 feet apart. They strike north 15 to 30 east and dip 60 west to 80 east. All have been productive. A fifth vein, a silicified breccia zone, has produced little or no ore. One of the quartz veins cuts back and forth across the contact between argillite and granodiorite. The others are in argillite.

Jim and Frances Jackson operated the mine under a lease agreement during 1951 through 1965. Boaz Mining Company, formed by Arthur J. Theis, Jack Fox, and James P. Jackson, Jr. owned the mine. Wm. Casey, one of the founders of United Parcel Service, had an interest and was a good friend of the Jacksons. Jim Jackson managed the mine and mill operations. Frances ran the cookhouse, which was in the Jacksons' home, serving three all-you-could-eat family-style meals a day for the crew and also providing room and board for occasional visitors. The writer was one of the latter.

Jackson's mine and mill operation employed himself and five or sometimes six other men. The crew worked 10 days on and four off. During winter months when deep snow blocked the road from McCully Fork to the mine, a snow cat was used for transportation. The workers left their personal vehicles at McCully Fork for use in getting to and from their homes, some in Sumpter and some in Baker City. The mine had electric power and telephone service, which were interrupted occasionally when wind or heavy snows caused trees to fall across the transmission lines.

Buffalo Mine, Harmon Roop hand mucking after broken ore from a previous dynamite blast had been machine loaded into ore cars and taken to the mill. Roop's job here was to rid the work area of loose rock so another round of blast holes could be drilled and loaded with dynamite. The light colored rock above Roop is part of the gold-bearing quartz vein being mined

Ore from the mine was crushed and ground and the sulfide minerals and gold were separated from the waste material (concentrated) in a 1.5 tons-per-hour flotation mill. Ratio of concentration averaged about 9 to1 (i.e. nine parts sulfide minerals and gold to one part waste rock). Concentrates averaged 9 ounces of gold and 68 ounces of silver per ton. Periodically, the mill concentrate was shipped to a smelter at Tacoma, Washington, where the gold and silver were extracted. This process recovered over 90 percent of the gold and silver from the ore that was mined. The smelter paid the Jacksons for the gold and silver that were recovered minus smelting and handling costs.

By 1958, the Jacksons had mined all of the developed ore on the 400 foot and higher levels of the mine. Post 1958 work has been confined to exploration and development of the veins on the 500 and 600 levels. Gold production has been small and sporadic. The Jacksons left the mine in 1965. Their production totaled 9,915 tons of ore averaging $43.50 per ton.

The Union Pacific Railroad's Natural Resources Division leased the mine in 1965 and reopened the long abandoned 600-foot adit level, 200 feet lower on the mountainside, in a failed attempt to find additional ore that could be mined. Rehabilitation of the 600-foot level was continued in 1979-1982 by the Buffalo Mining Company, a group of Seattle investors. The flotation mill was also revamped then operated sporadically during part of 1980-1982. The ore was from exploration work on the 600- and 500-foot levels of the mine. Several subsequent attempts to reactivate the mine have led to very little production.

La Belleview Mill, Granite District

La Belleview Mine

The La Belleview Mine, also known as LaBellevue, is located three miles northeast of the Buffalo near the head of Onion Creek. It was one of the very few mines in eastern Oregon where silver exceeded gold in production value. The deposit was discovered in 1876 by John and Fred Cabell. They built and used an arrastra to produce a small amount of free gold. David Keith and J. T. Bamberger of Salt Lake City, Utah acquired the property in 1890. The Bamberger Brothers had an interest in the property as late as 1941. "The mine produced $500,000 during 1878-1892, 1927-1929, and 1939-1941. About 6,000 feet of underground development work has been done, including four adits over a vertical range of 600 feet. Total production to 1911 amounted to 8,000 tons grossing $200,000. The 4,800 tons treated in 1940 yielded 811 ounces of gold, 40,444 ounces of silver, 8,243 pounds of copper and 33,732 pounds of lead" (Brooks and Ramp, 1968, p. 65). The 1939-1941 operations utilized a 50-tons-per day flotation mill. R. B. McGinnis was the mine manager during the 1927-1929 and 1939-1941 periods of operation."

Cougar-Independence

The Cougar and Independence mines are about a mile apart on opposites sides of the ridge west of Granite Creek about three miles north of Granite. During their last years of operation they were jointly owned and ore from both mines was treated in the same mill, a flotation plant on Granite

Creek able to process 80 tons per day. The Cougar Mine is about one half mile west of the mill site. The Independence Mine is about one mile northwest of the Cougar. Owners at one time included Irving and Langdon Rand. Irving was an Attorney in Portland and Baker City. Mrs. Irving Rand (Helen) wrote the book *Gold, Jade and Elegance* about people and events in early-day Baker County. Helen Rand was related to W. H. Packwood, prominent eastern Oregon pioneer and his great-grandson, Bob Packwood, U. S. Senator from Oregon in the 1960s and 1970s.

The Cougar produced 19,126 ounces of gold and 10,976 ounces of silver from 51,500 tons of ore in 1938-1942.The Independence mine produced 3,209 ounces of gold and 14, 582 ounces of silver from about 9,500 tons of ore produced during four periods of operation between 1907-1940. Ore from the 1938-1940 period was treated in the Cougar mill.

Cougar Indepndence Mine and Mill.

In 1974, W. A. Bowes and Associates began work to reopen the Cougar Mine and the nearby New York Mine. Equipment for heap leach cyanidation of ore from the two mines was installed at the Cougar Mine, including a 280 feet by 90 feet asphalt pad and tailings storage pond. Work in 1978 included running a decline 1700 feet long to intersect the Cougar vein about 200 feet beneath the old pre-1942 workings. Bowes and Associates intersected the Cougar vein but apparently failed to find enough ore to justify continuing work. The company dropped its lease on the properties in late summer 1981.

Monumental Mine

The Monumental is near the head of Granite Creek, seven miles north of Granite. Tabor's (1988) story regarding early development of the mine reflects a great example of getting the cart before the horse. Rich silver ore was found in an outcropping vein and claims were located covering the discovery. One ton of the ore sent to San Francisco yielded $1,500 in gold and silver. Following that good news, the property owners sold enough stock to pay for installing a 20-stamp mill costing $72,000, sinking a 100 ft shaft, building a three story hotel, sawmill, assay office and other buildings, and hiring 100 men to run the mine and mill. Unfortunately, after a very short period of operation, it was determined that there was too little gold and silver in the ore to sustain further development. Subsequent efforts to operate the mine under new management led to little production (Tabor, 1988, p.34-35).

Quotes from Swartley (1914, p.139) add details to the story: The mine "shipped 14 tons of ore to San Francisco in 1874....The production to date is reported to be approximately $100,000...the lenses of ore have a maximum width of 18 inches and stope lengths of less than 100 feet." Production of $100,000 certainly would not have paid for all the work that was done.

Monumental Mine. Horse-operated hoist, sometimes used in initial stages of prospecting a mineralized vein. If the vein proves subeconomic, the cost of building construction is saved.

Other Mines, Granite District

The geologic map of the Granite quadrangle by Brooks and others (1982) shows the location of 77 mines and prospects in the quadrangle. Few of them have produced significant amounts of gold.

Oregon Metal Mines Handbook, Bulletin 14-B, Oregon State Department of Geology and Mineral Industries, 1941 gives brief descriptions of about a dozen small mines and prospects in the Granite District that are not mentioned above. Ajax Mine on Lucas Gulch produced $40,000 from a 90 ft long section of the Ajax vein in 1905-06.

Left: Bourne street scene.

Right: Damaged photo of Independence Mill and mining camp, Granite District. Typed below the picture: "Ore mill and camp of the Cougar-Independence Mine three miles above Granite. Taken by Langdon Rand."

Independence Mining Camp, Granite District

Above: Monumental Mill, started 1872.
Below: Monumental Mine.

Above: Chinese walls on Granite Creek three miles north of the town of Granite.
Below: Chinese walls along Union Creek, near present Phillips Reservoir.
Chinese wall photos courtesy of Baker City Herald.

View of Cable Cove with mines and prospects dotting its slopes. Baldy Mountain is high point of the ridge. Left to right, the mines are California Mill, Herculean, Standard, Black Dwarf, California Mine Tunnel No. 7, The Miner, and Crown Point Mines. J.W. Cowden photo, ca. 1910.

Left:California Mine, Cable Cove District. Stacked bags of gold ore concentrates ready for shipment to the smelter.

Cable Cove District

Several small mines and prospects dot the slopes of Cable Cove, an amphitheatre-shaped glacial cirque at the head of Silver Creek, a tributary of Cracker Creek about 12 miles north and west of Sumpter. The district straddles the Baker-Grant County line that here follows the divide between the Powder River drainage to the east and the North Fork of the John Day River to the west. To the west Baldy Mountain rises to 8,330 feet elevation. To the east the serrated peaks of the Elkhorn Range form the horizon.

From DOGAMI Bulletin 61: "At its widest part Cable Cove is roughly a mile and a half from rim to rim and about 800 feet deep. The inner slopes are steep and rocky. The outer slopes descend more gently north and west to the North Fork of the John Day River Elevations range from about 6,500 to more than 7,000 feet above sea level. The road up Silver Creek is ordinarily closed by snow from November through May."

Lode deposits in the district were first worked in the early 1870's. The main period of development was between 1899 and 1910. Production has been small, probably less than $200,000 although several veins are extensively developed The bulk of production is credited to the Imperial-Eagle, California, and Last Chance mines in order of their productive rank. The workings of the Imperial Eagle mine are said to aggregate about 10.000 feet. There is no record of placer gold production. The gold deposits of the Cable Cove district are in granodiorite of the Bald Mountain batholith. Basalt dikes are present but not abundant. Shearing in a northeasterly direction has developed a broad system of faults and shear zones in which the gold veins were formed.

Most of the mines worked veins made up of brecciated and intensely altered granodiorite interspersed with lenses and streaks of quartz and a little calcite. Pyrite and arsenopyrite are the chief metallic minerals. Lead and zinc sulfides are present locally. The gold values were confined mainly to portions of veins rich in pyrite and arsenopyrite. Much of the ore exceeded 10 percent sulfides. The Imperial-Eagle vein is traceable for more than 2 miles, and is as much as 25 feet wide. Ore shoots were rarely more then 2 feet wide, short, and unpredictably located.

Cracker Creek District

The Cracker Creek District contains much of the area drained by Cracker Creek and McCully Fork, which join at the northwest corner of Sumpter and become the Powder River. The district includes the highly productive North Pole-Columbia lode and numerous lesser veins of a system that extends southwesterly from the head of Rock Creek on the Elkhorn Ridge divide to the Ibex mine at the head of Deep Creek on the North Fork of the John Day River divide. Production from lode mines in the district has been about $9,000,000 in gold and silver of which about $8,000,000 came from the North Pole-Columbia lode. Most of the district is covered by geologic maps of the Bourne quadrangle by Brooks and others (1982) and the Mt. Ireland quadrangle by Ferns and others (1982). These maps show the locations of more than 50 lode mines and prospects in the Cracker Creek District. For most of them there are no records of production

The district is underlain mainly by dark-colored siliceous to tuffaceous argillite of the Elkhorn Ridge Argillite. Volcanic greenstone and small limestone pods are interbedded with argillite in places. Also present locally are large fault bounded blocks of metagabbro.

The southern contact of the Bald Mountain batholith extends along the northern edge of the district and the gold bearing veins tend to parallel that contact and to dip steeply southeast. Dikes related to the latter intrusive are intruded into rocks of the argillite series in many places. Most of the gold deposits occur along steep northeast-trending faults in argillite. Some, such as the Mountain View, Argonaut, and Mammoth veins, are very near the granodiorite contact and locally, for example at the Argonaut, cut the granodiorite.

North Pole-Columbia Lode

The North Pole-Columbia lode is traceable for about 4 1\2 miles. It crosses Cracker Creek about a half mile west of the old town site of Bourne. It has a productive strike length of 12,000 feet, extending about equally northeast and southwest from Cracker Creek. The productive mines in the ore zone are from north to south, the North Pole, Eureka and Excelcior (better known as the E and E), Taber Fraction, Columbia, and Golconda. Total production is about 370,000 ounces of gold and $190,000 of silver.

Vertical extent of mining is about 2,500 feet from the upper levels of the North Pole mine to the bottom of the Columbia shaft which is 918 feet deep. A large part of the lode within 1,000 feet of the surface remains unexplored.

Pardee (1909) concluded that the North Pole-Columbia lode occupies a fault zone along which there was about 1,800 feet of horizontal movement and 400 feet of vertical movement. The lode dips steeply southeast. Widths range from 10 feet to 300 feet and average about 25 feet. Outcrops locally project as much as 30 feet above ground level on Golconda ground.

Sumpter, Granite Street. Now a small village of 200 population, Sumpter was once the hub of the most productive gold mining region in northeastern Oregon. At least 25 lode mines and many placers were active. Maps by Brooks and others (Bourne quadrangle1982a and Granite quadrangle1982b) and Ferns and others (Elkhorn Peak quadrangle 1987) show the location of 61 lode mines and prospects in the Bourne quadrangle, most of which have produced little or no gold or silver.

Middle: Sumpter looking east across Cracker Creek.

Bottom: Sumpter looking south.

The lode is tabular body composed of fragmented argillite and chert that were crushed along the fault and then re-cemented by quartz and ore minerals. The quartz and metallic ore minerals, consisting mainly of pyrite, arsenopyrite, gold, and silver were deposited from hot fluids or gases that rose along the fault from a deep magma source. The productive part of the lode consists mainly of irregular and overlapping bands and lenses of silicified argillite and chert breccia, quartz, and fault gouge (brecciated rock altered largely to clay). Some of the quartz replaced the country rock and some was deposited in fractures and other open spaces. Evidently the quartz deposition was sporadic and repeatedly interrupted by brecciation. Sulfide minerals and gold and silver were deposited locally near the end of the mineralization process. The ore occured as overlapping shoots mostly along the footwall of the lode. The average width of mined ore shoots is between 4 and 6 feet.

Reports by Pardee and Hewett (1914) and Swartley (1914) indicate that the best gold and silver values were in silicified argillite. Massive quartz contained very little gold. Sulfides, chiefly pyrite, typically comprise a small percentage of the ore. Other sulfides include arsenopyrite, marcasite, chalcopyrite, tetrahedrite stibnite, galena, sphalerite, pyrargyrite, antimonite, schwatzite and cinnabar. Gold telluride minerals are rare. Calcite, roscoelite, chalcopyrite and arsenopyrite, either singly or together are typical components of the rich ore but their presence did not necessarily indicate high values. Practically all the gold and silver is in the sulfide minerals, chiefly arsenopyrite and to a lesser extent pyrite and chalcopyrite.

The Golconda, Columbia, and E and E mines each had 20-stamp mills. The mill at the North Pole mine had 30 stamps. Average operating capacity of the 20-stamp mills was about 50 tons per day and of the 30-stamp mill, about 65 tons. Only about 67 percent of the gold was recovered from ore milled from these mines because much of it was contained in sulfide minerals that the primitive mills of those days could not concentrate efficiently. Modern mills, being more than 95 percent efficient, could have saved an additional $3,000,000 worth of gold.

All five of the major mines along the lode were closed by the end of 1916. Each in turn shut down because their operations became unprofitable. Costs of mining were rising and the difficulties of treating the ore increased as the mine workings were extended to greater depths. Part of the cost difficulty was that each of the mines was a separate entity with different owners. Each had its own mill, mining equipment, and management staff. Had the properties been consolidated and worked as one mine, production likely would have lasted considerably longer. Efforts to consolidate tthe operations were unsuccessful largely because the owners were absentee. They were active in affairs related to banking, publishing, politics, and industry and had little knowledge of mining. Baring Brothers of London owned the North Pole (Eastern Oregon Gold Mining Co.). Jonathan Bourne and associates of Portland, Oregon, owned the Bourne Gold Mining Co., which owned and operated the E&E Mine. The Columbia (Columbia Gold Mining Co.) was owned by Edward W. Backus and two other men of Minneapolis, Minnesota, and Frank S. Baillie of Sumpter, Oregon. The Golconda was owned by Mr. C. S. Jackson, the well-known owner of the Portland Daily Journal, Portland, Oregon. Baillie, who was the managing engineer of the Columbia mine, was the only owner having significant experience in mining.

Mines on the Bald Mountain-Ibex vein in the western part of the Cracker Creek District and their estimated production (Hewett, 1931, pp. 318-321; Ferms, et al, 1982) are Mammoth, $40,000; Belle of Baker, $400,000; Bald Mountain-Ibex, 9,000 ounces of gold and 90,000 ounces of silver

Three views of the Sumpter Smelter, located about 1/2 mile south of Sumpter city. Sumpter Smelter, built in 1903, began operating in late 1904, about the time lode mining was beginning to wane. It shut down after about three years for lack of ore to mill.

Upper: Sumpter Smelter in winter.

Right: Distant view looking south.

Below: smelter with Sumpter Valley Railroad switch in foreground.

Above: Sumpter ca. 1895, when the population was about 150.

Below: Sumpter, ca. 1900. Smoke from many chimneys indicates the weather was a bit chilly..

from 30,000 tons of ore.

The Bald Mountain-Ibex vein is traceable for about three miles, strikes N 25 to 60 degrees E, dips 60 to 80 degrees SE, varies from 5 to 25 feet wide, and is composed of bands and lenses of crushed argillite and chert cemented by quartz and a little calcite. Sulfides are mainly pyrite and arsenopyrite. The vein was extensively explored in the early 1980s. More than 65,000 feet of diamond drilling was done, 3,200 feet of underground workings were reopened, and 2,000 feet of new underground work was completed before the partners concluded that the amount of potentially available ore was not enough to justify further development. Cost of the drilling, mine rehabilitation, and new work exceeded $6,000,000. Many small companies were involved at one time or another. American Copper and Nickel, Inc., which became an operating partner in 1984, was the last.

In 1980, a consortium of Brooks Minerals, Inc., and Amax Exploration, Inc., acquired the property and began reopening the old E and E and North Pole Mines. By the end of 1982, approximately 5,000 feet of level workings and 500 feet of raises in the North Pole and E and E mines had been rehabilitated and 3,000 feet of new underground work done. The Jevne adit had been driven 600 feet. Work stopped on September 22, 1982, when Amax withdrew. Brooks Minerals personnel said that expenses to date amounted to about $5.5 million, with an additional $14 million work planned in mine development, mill construction and completion of the Jevne adit. Proven and probable reserves totaled 121,000 tons and 135,000 tons, averaging 0.3 ounces per ton gold.

Sumpter

Sumpter, now a small village of 200 population, was once the hub of the most productive gold mining region in northeastern Oregon. At least 25 lode mines and many placers were active. Maps by Brooks and others (Bourne quadrangle 1982a and Granite quadrangle 1982b) and Ferns and others (Elkhorn Peak quadrangle, 1987) show the location of 61 lode mines and prospects in the Bourne quadrangle, most of which have produced little or no gold or silver.

Brooks Hawley (1978) says gold was discovered in gravel deposits near the forks of Cracker Creek and McCully Fork in 1862. The locators were five prospectors from the southeastern U. S. named Hugh Asbury, John Reel, Fletcher Henderson, Bill Flanagan, and Dick Johnson. They built a cabin and, being southern sympathizers, they called the site Fort Sumter.

Apparently, placer deposits operable by hand and hydraulic methods were not plentiful so Sumpter's boom waited for lode mines to be developed beginning in the mid-1890's and the arrival of the Sumpter Valley Rairoad in 1896. Those events led to a mining and building boom in that area that lasted until about 1910. Sumpter's population exploded to 3,000 or 4,000 in spring 1900, up from about 150 in August 1898. Many of the most productive lode mines of the region were developed during this period while much money was unwisely invested in worthless prospects. The sudden population increase was fostered by wildly exaggerated predictions regarding the impending growth of the mining and timber industries in the surrounding region made by General Charles S. Warren. He and W. C. Calder formed the Sumpter Townsite Syndicate (photo) in August, 1899. The Syndicate turned a large profit by buying and reselling 100 choice lots in the townsite and 600 acres of prime land alongside the townsite that they had subdivided. Sumpter lost most of its downtown area to fire on August 13, 1917, and never recovered because the large lode mines in the

Sumpter. Pack train about 1900.

Sumpter. Freight wagons perhaps headed for mining towns such as Greenhorn and Granite with supplies off loaded from the Sumpter Valley Railroad.

area had closed. The Columbia had shut down in 1916, the last to close of the five major mines on the North Pole Columbia Lode.

Sumpter Dredges

Large bucketline dredges began operating in Sumpter Valley in 1913. Three different ones were built and operated and one or another of them was active during most of the time between 1913 and 1924 and 1935-1954. Sumpter Dredge Number 3 began work in 1935 and, except for a three-year shutdown in W.W.II, operated continuously until 1954. It sits today in a pond on the south edge of Sumpter where it has been since 1954 when dredging in Oregon ended. A newly constructed depot near the dredge is the western terminus of the new five miles long Sumpter Valley Railroad. The park and the railroad are monuments to the years of donated time and effort of many people who chose to not let history die by preserving artifacts of the mining and timber industries.

The dredge was electrically operated. It has 72 nine-cubic foot buckets and dug to a depth of 18 feet. It employed 20 to 30 people. All of the dredges combined covered 2,603 acres and handled 60,000,000 yards of gravel. Recorded output was 297,000 ounces of gold and 71,000 ounces of silver. Smaller dragline dredges worked the gravels in Cracker Creek above Sumpter at about the same time the Bucket line dredges were active in Sumpter Valley. For about 8 miles along Powder River below Sumpter almost the entire width of the mile-wide valley has been mined by bucketline dredges.

Dragline dredges and washing plants worked the gravels in the lower parts of Cracker Creek and McCully Fork above Sumpter in 1938-1942. They produced 22,000 ounces of gold from about 3.5 million yards of gravel. Gravel deposits in the upper parts of these creeks and parts of their tributaries including Buck Gulch and Mammoth Gulch were worked earlier by hand and hydraulic methods. On the adjacent slopes, bench gravels and scattered remnants of gravel from an ancient Early Tertiary drainage system were the source of considerable placer gold (Pardee and Hewett, 1941). The Downie placer is credited with production of 4,000 ounces of gold, from terrace gravel of McCully Fork. (Ferns and others, 1982).

DOGAMI Bulletin 14-A (1939) says that Little, Harris and Wolfinger Dredge Co. had been operating a 1½-yard dragline and floating washing plant on L.R. Harris property near Sumpter since October, 1938, digging about 2,000 yards per day. Harris had worked there for several years previously with shovel and washing plant on skids. The Little, Harris and Wolfinger, and Nutting Doodlebugs took out about $700,000 (Hawley notes).

A Monighan dragline, the oldest walking dragline known to exist, was employed by Northwest Development Co. in the Sumpter area from 1940 to 1942. The machine was built between 1925-1927 and used many years at gravel operations in Colorado until purchased and brought to Sumpter in 1940 by H. R. Nutting. He and three other mine owners, Fred Little, Rodi Harris, and Harry Wolfinger, combined properties and equipment, including three draglines, smaller than the Monighan, under the name Northwest Development Company. The Monighan was used mainly to move overburden. It had a 3-yard bucket, an 80-foot boom and a 40- to 45-foot reach and could dig deeper and move more gravel than other draglines they had. That company operated until 1942, when the Government ordered mining activity stopped in order to free up men for the draft and war industries.

Sumpter area dredging

Upper right: Monighan Dragline employed by Northwest Development Company. The dragline remains in the Sumpter area, with plans to restore it to working condition.

Right and below: Sumpter Valley Dredge Number 3, operating about 1941. Brooks Hawley ranch in background.

Bourne

Bourne, now a small ghost town adjacent to Cracker Creek six miles north of Sumpter, Oregon, saw more prosperous and wilder days when the mines along the North Pole-Columbia Lode were producing gold. The town was started in the 1880's. Between 1890 and 1910 it was one of the leading gold mining camps of the West with a population of about 750. At one time, more than 1,500 people got their mail at the Bourne post office. This figure includes residents at mines and mine-related activities such as sawmills in the surrounding region.

The initial discoverers of gold in the area included men from the southeastern U. S. who were sometimes called "crackers." Thence the first settlement was called Cracker, the creek running through it was named Cracker Creek, and the surrounding area was called the Cracker Creek Mining District. Later, the town was renamed for Jonathan Bourne, who owned the E & E mine in its hey-day. Bourne was born in Bedford, Massachusetts, February 23, 1855, graduated from Harvard in 1877, came to Portland in 1878, and was admitted to the Oregon Bar in 1880. He served in the Oregon House of Representatives (1887-1899) and one term as U.S. Senator from Oregon (1907-1913). After his Senate term, he lived in Washington, D.C., until his death in 1940.

Bourne was notorious as headquarters for swindlers, the most flagrant being J. Wallace White, whose Sampson Company, Ltd., with offices in Bourne, New York, and London, bilked gullible investors world wide out of at least $5 million. White lived part time in a dazzling white mansion he built in 1906 with part of his loot on the hillside above Bourne.

As the mines along the North Pole-Columbia lode closed, the population of Bourne dwindled. The 1910 census counted 70 people. After the Columbia mine closed in 1916, sporadic activity at some of the smaller lode mines and placers in the district kept the town barely alive for several more years. Bourne post office, established in 1895, was discontinued in 1927. Most of the buildings were destroyed in a 1937 flood. A few cabins and tumbled-down buildings mark the place of the old town.

Some mining was done on the North Pole-Columbia lode in the late 1930s and early 1940s. John Arthur had charge of the property and part of it was subleased to Meyer and Engle. A news article (July 30. 1942) reported that one of the richest strikes in the history of the Baker mining region had been found in the Taber Fraction mine. About 19 sacks of the high grade ore were taken out of a spot about seven feet in length and several inches in thickness. The article further reported that sub-leasees of the Columbia, Taber Fraction, and other parts of the Bourne mines had been shipping ore to the smelter for the past three years. Arthur was instrumental in construction of a new mill completed about 1942 on the old E and E mill site. These operations were terminated by government order in late 1942.

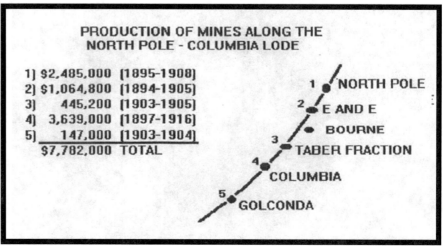

PRODUCTION OF MINES ALONG THE
NORTH POLE - COLUMBIA LODE

1]	$2,485,000	[1895-1908]
2]	$1,064,800	[1894-1905]
3]	445,200	[1903-1905]
4]	3,639,000	[1897-1916]
5]	147,000	[1903-1904]
	$7,782,000	TOTAL

1 NORTH POLE
2 E AND E
3 BOURNE
TABER FRACTION
4 COLUMBIA
5 GOLCONDA

Above, and below, Bourne, Cracker Creek District, 1905.

Above: Sumpter. Boiler headed for Midway Mine, Ibex District.

Above: E & E Mill, one-half mile up Cracker Creek from the present ghost town of Bourne.

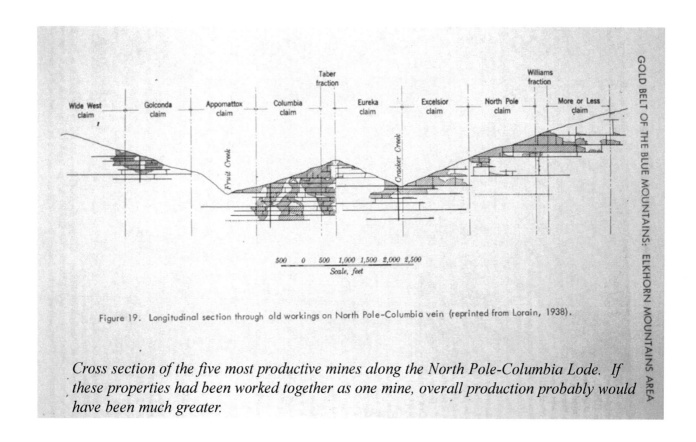

GOLD BELT OF THE BLUE MOUNTAINS: ELKHORN MOUNTAINS AREA

Figure 19. Longitudinal section through old workings on North Pole-Columbia vein (reprinted from Lorain, 1938).

Cross section of the five most productive mines along the North Pole-Columbia Lode. If these properties had been worked together as one mine, overall production probably would have been much greater.

Left and above: Golconda Mine and Mill, Cracker Creek District.

Right: North Pole Mill, Cracker Creek District, with sacks of hi-grade ore from North Pole Mine.

Below: North Pole Mine.

Above: Bourne. E & E Mine (Eureka & Excelsior), dark buildings near the top of the draw above town.

Left: Columbia Mine.

Below: A closer view of Columbia Mine mill.

Above: The Baisley-Elkhorn Mine. Photo is faded and damaged.

Rock Creek District

The Rock Creek District includes the upper Rock Creek and Pine Creek drainages on the eastern slope of Elkhorn Ridge overlooking Baker Valley. Principle mines are the Baisley-Elkhorn and Highland-Maxwell. The principal mine workings are in steep terrane between 5,500 and 7,000 ft elevation, although some of the veins apex at much higher elevations. Baisley Elkhorn and Highland Maxwell are two of a large cluster of more than 30 mines and prospects along the contact between granodiorite of the Bald Mountain batholith and hornfelsed argillite of the Elkhorn Ridge argillite formation. The Rock Creek District includes the upper parts of Rock Creek and Pine Creek, which head close together in the high mountains northwest of Baker City. Here Elkhorn Ridge culminates in a straggling network of ridges and peaks, some of which tower more than 5,000 feet above Baker Valley. Elevations range from, 5,500 to 8,500 feet. *(See Ferns and others, 1987.)*

The intrusive contact between granodiorite of the Bald Mountain batholith to the north and rocks of the Elkhorn Ridge argillite to the south extends easterly through the district.. The intruded rocks are mainly dark colored argillite that, near the contact, have been altered to fine-grained crystalline hornfels. A number of quartz veins occur along or close to the argillite-granodiorite contact. Some are in argillite, some are in granodiorite and others cross the contact. This system of veins strikes northeast and connects with the Cracker Creek system on the southwest. Past production of the Rock Creek District is credited largely to the Baisley-Elkhorn and Highland- Maxwell mines, whose combined output totals more than $1,560,000 (about $1.8 million says Ferns, et al 1987). There is no record of placer gold production from the district. Nearly $8,000,000 worth of chemical grade lime and crushed limestone from the Baboon Creek and Marble Creek quarries, also was mined within the district.

Baisley-Elkhorn Mine

The Baisley-Elkhorn Mine is on the North Fork of Pine Creek about 18 miles northwest of Baker City. The last several miles are by primitive dirt road.

Newspapers of the time reported that the Baisley-Elkhorn gold-bearing vein was discovered by one of the Baisley brothers, Jerry or Jim, in 1882. He found the vein while hunting elk in the upper Pine Creek area. He marked the spot with a large set of elk horns he found nearby, then carried a few pieces of the rock to his home. About a year later he got around to panning some of the quartz and found that it contained an interesting amount of gold. The brothers went to the elk-horn-marked spot. They reported that the vein was traceable for a mile and a half. They located claims and began mining where the vein was most prominantly exposed. Their brother Sam, who had considerable mining experience, built an arrastra and mill and began producing gold. He claimed to have cleaned up $7,100 in 71 days.

According to Lindgren (1901) the Baisley-Elkhorn vein was discovered about 1882 and a mill was built on the property in 1889. For several years the vein was worked by separate mines, the Baisley-Elkhorn and Robbins-Elkhorn. (Brooks and Ramp, 1968). Around 1900 the two properties were consolidated. Since 1907 there has been little production although during the 1920's considerable exploration work was done. A small output was made in the 1930's. The following production figures are from Pardee and Hewett (1914, p. 74). No record of 1901-1904 output, if any, has been found. However, BMA 12-26-03 says Baisley-Elkhorn again shipping concentrate from a mill long idle.

Prior to Jan. 1, 1898	$342,861.07
1898 to Dec. 1, 1900	84,591.64
26,095 tons of crude ore (bullion)	
3,759 tons concentrates	239,529.84
472 tons shipped at $45.03 per ton	21,254.04
1905: 20,000 tons crude ore, yielding	
3,000 tons concentrates	210,000.00
1907: 7,680 tons crude ore yielding	
1,280 tons concentrates	38,481.00
1912 Small production	?

Total	$936,717.59

The Baisley-Elkhorn Mine is developed by 10,000 feet of underground workings. Most of the ore produced was via a 626-foot adit crosscut to the vein and a 400-foot underground shaft with workings on 4 levels. The lowest working level is 665 feet below the outcrop (Pardee and Hewett,

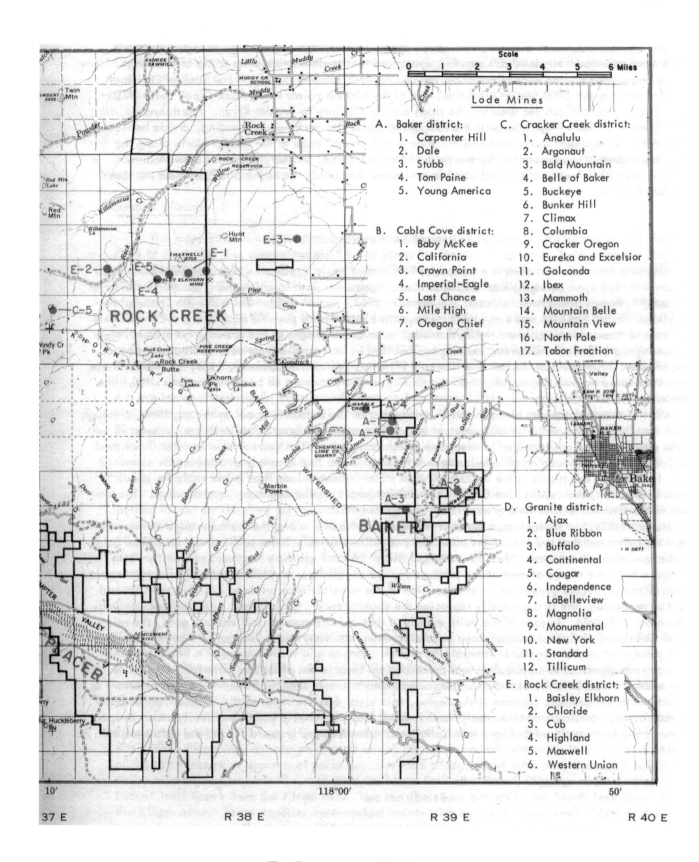

Scale

Lode Mines

A. Baker district:
1. Carpenter Hill
2. Dale
3. Stubb
4. Tom Paine
5. Young America

B. Cable Cove district:
1. Baby McKee
2. California
3. Crown Point
4. Imperial-Eagle
5. Last Chance
6. Mile High
7. Oregon Chief

C. Cracker Creek district:
1. Analulu
2. Argonaut
3. Bald Mountain
4. Belle of Baker
5. Buckeye
6. Bunker Hill
7. Climax
8. Columbia
9. Cracker Oregon
10. Eureka and Excelsior
11. Golconda
12. Ibex
13. Mammoth
14. Mountain Belle
15. Mountain View
16. North Pole
17. Tabor Fraction

D. Granite district:
1. Ajax
2. Blue Ribbon
3. Buffalo
4. Continental
5. Cougar
6. Independence
7. LaBelleview
8. Magnolia
9. Monumental
10. New York
11. Standard
12. Tillicum

E. Rock Creek district:
1. Baisley Elkhorn
2. Chloride
3. Cub
4. Highland
5. Maxwell
6. Western Union

Index map Baker
and Rock Creek Districts

Above and below: Baisley-Elkhorn mining crew.

1914). Exploration work done during the 1920s includes a 2,300-foot crosscut adit and a long drift on the vein 950 feet below the vein outcrop and 285 feet below the lowest shaft level. Lindgren (1901) said the Baisley-Elkhorn mine developed a near vertical vein consisting mainly of crushed granodiorite with streaks of quartz and coarse sulfides.

Descendents of the Baisley brothers remain in the Baker City area. Wretha Hudson said Sam Baisley and his father mined gold from placer deposits in the Virtue area and near the Nelson placer.

Highland-Maxwell Mine, Rock Creek District

Highland Mine on the west of Elkhorn ridge and Maxwell Mine on the east are separate but contiguous mines or claim blocks on the same vein. Development began about 1900. The two mines were worked separately until 1921. Highland produced about $375,000 and Maxwell about $100,000. They then were idle until 1935. Both were rehabilitated and then jointly operated from April 1936 to some time in the 1940s. John Arthur was involved in the operation in June, 1938.

Under certain conditions and proper snow depth, roads were ignored and concentrates were hauled to Haines via sled—all down hill, which meant the horses were able to pull large loads. The combined properties are developed by 15,000 feet of workings (sounds excessive) (Pardee and Hewett, 1914), including many adits and a shaft from the lowest adit level for an estimated production of $625,000.

Auburn

Wegars (1995) said a major gold strike was made on May 2, 1862, in a gulch, later named Blue Canyon, about four miles south of Griffin Gulch. A townsite named Auburn was established there and by mid-July as many as 300 people may have been living there. There were three stores, two saloons, two blacksmith shops, three butcher shops, one boarding house, and several dwellings. Many other business buildings and dwellings were in construction or planning stages (p.32). Auburn became the county seat when Baker County was established September 22, 1862, carved from Wasco County which until then included all of Oregon east of the Cascades.

According to Hiatt (1893), Auburn's population in October 1862, including miners camped in every nearby gulch and emigrants camped in the valley below amounted to between 4,000 and 6,000 people and probably exceeded for a short time the population of Portland which totaled 2,874 people in the 1860 census.

Patera (1994, p. 10) says that at its zenith Auburn had "a mile-long main street with a few side streets where topography permitted. It was laid out with fifty five blocks, and by the time the post office was authorized on November 1, 1862 it contained a motley assortment of over 500 buildings and was developing the social structure of a real town, with parties and balls - and an occasional murder."

The *Walla Walla Statesman* of October 25, 1862, printed a letter from a correspondent who signed himself "Mack": "Auburn, Oct. 20th, 1862. Auburn is still improving. There are about three hundred buildings now completed in the city. There is one brick yard in successful operation here, and there are three sawmills on the road to this place. There is a school here, and it is well attended.... Provisions are becoming more plentiful and are still arriving every day...."

By 1865, Auburn's population had declined to about 150 and some residents were cutting abandoned buildings into firewood. Of those who left Auburn, many went looking for gold elsewhere in eastern Oregon and western Idaho. The rush to Idaho's Boise Basin mining camps drew heavily from Auburn's population beginning in late 1862. Many early arrivals in Auburn were farmers who acquired land claims in the valleys and raised crops and livestock to feed the miners and their followers. They were involved in establishing farm and ranch communities in or on the edges of the valleys, including La Grande, Union, Haines, Richland, Halfway, Durkee, Huntington, Unity and Hereford.

The population of Auburn declined rapidly for two reasons: 1) there was not enough gold–bearing ground or water enough to work the claims to support more than a fraction of the would-be miners (this was true of many early mining camps) and 2) Auburn was built in a very poor location several miles off logical routes of travel through the region and where winters are cold and snow is deep. The post office at Auburn lingered until 1903.

Parts of nearly every creek and gulch in the area along the southeast extension of Elkhorn Ridge north and west of Auburn

Right: The gravestone of Henry Griffin. Griffin was buried in the cemetery of the town he helped found, Auburn, Oregon, now completely gone except for a stone basement and a couple of ancient but hardy apple trees.

Below: Isaac Hiatt's sketch of the first cabin in Auburn. The cabin was probably located in Griffin Gulch near where the first gold was found by Henry Griffin.

Sketch by Isaac Hiatt

Left: Log cabins in Auburn, set on pilings to allow for deep snow in winter.

Below: Auburn Blacksmithing. The shop was built of rough sawn lumber. The first sawmill was brought to Auburn in 1862 by I. B. Bowen.

show the effects of past placer mining activity, including Blue Canyon, French Gulch, and California Gulch near Auburn, Elk Creek, Washington Gulch, and Salmon Creek north of Auburn, and Miners Creek, and Deer Creek to the west. Some of the early-day placers were described as "enourmously rich" (Swartley, 1914) but production records are scarce. Some, notably Elk Creek, are still active on a small scale.

Auburn Ditch, 30 miles long, was started in 1862, extending from Blue Canyon near Auburn northward along the eastern front of Elkhorn Ridge to a reservoir built on Goodrich Creek. Auburn Ditch furnished water to the mines in the Auburn area. W. H. Packwood, one of the first to arrive in the Auburn area, was instrumental in the construction and management of the Auburn Ditch and several other placer mining ditches in the northeastern Oregon gold belt. Auburn Ditch and Goodrich Reservoir are now part of the Baker City water system.

Head (1987) mentioned three ditches that carried water along the eastern slope of Elkhorn Ridge into the Griffin Gulch-Auburn area and also to Salmon Creek. The earliest, extending from Elk Creek to the mines on Griffin Gulch, was completed on May 20, 1862. The second was built by Carter and Davidson from Elk Creek to French Gulch (Auburn) with the intake being below the head of Littlefield's Ditch. The third extended from Goodrich Reservoir to Auburn.

Some placer mines in the Auburn region are said in early reports to have been "enormously rich." The Nelson Placer on Salmon Creek produced in excess of $400,000 prior to 1914, but no records of early day production from other mines are available. Swartley (1914, p. 163) said the Auburn placers were practically exhausted, but elsewhere in the region placers were being worked on a small scale.

Below: Baker City ca. 1865

Baker City, ca. 1875

Baker City, ca. 1900. Photo from Old Reservoir Hill. Note baseball diamond in fore-ground, Chinatown with Joss House, center, and the taller buildings downtown. The high school is in the upper left center.

Baker City, ca. 1910, Main (then called Front) Street. Note the Heilner store (now Neuberger Heilner) with cupola on the left (west) and the Geiser Grand cupola on the right side (east) of the street. Note also Baker City's ongoing love affair with awnings on downtown store fronts.

Baker City

The town named Baker City, first settled in 1864, was chartered in October 1874. The first post office was established on March 27, 1866, with William McCrary first post master. It and Baker County were named for Edward Baker, Oregon's first Senator, a close friend of President Abraham Lincoln, and the only member of congress killed in the Civil War. He died in the Battle of Balls Bluff, in 1861. The Baker City name changed to Baker in 1911 then back to Baker City again in 1985. The city had trolley car lines and an Opera House, etc.

Among the first buildings in Baker City was a 10-stamp mill built in 1864 to extract gold from ore hauled in by wagons from the Virtue mine east of town, a distance of seven miles. The mill was powered by running water from a ditch connecting with the Powder River. About 1874, after having found ample water to run a mill in the under ground workings, the company erected a 20-stamp mill at the mine thus avoiding the seven-mile wagon journey into Baker City. By the fall of 1865 as the gold was running out and Auburn was fading, miners and their followers were moving to other camps while many businesses moved to Baker City, which was growing as the mercantile center for the farms and ranches in Baker and surrounding valleys.

The county seat was moved from Auburn to Baker City in 1868. The 1870 census for Baker County provides the following statistics: White males 1,457; white females, 523; non-white males 665; non-white females, 18; Total 2,663. There were 877 dwellings and 777 families. For 1880, the number for Baker County was 4,642 and for Baker City, 815. In 1900, Baker City population was about 6,700. Following the advent of the railroad in 1884 that facilitated a lode-mining boom that lasted until about 1910, Baker City population jumped from 815 in 1880 to 6,663 in 1890 and about 8,000 in 1900. During those days Baker City was touted as the "Queen City of a rich mineral, live-stock, and timber producing empire." Mary Oman, in an unpublished Flagstaff Mine manuscript confirms, "Baker City population increased from 857 in 1865 to 1,687 in 1875 to 6,061 in 1895."

Lode mine production progressed rapidly after railroads reached Baker City in 1884 and Sumpter in 1896. Until 1887, when Malheur County was created, Baker County included Wallowa, Union, and Malheur Counties. Union and Wallowa counties were carved off in 1864. The state legislature made Baker City the county seat in 1866. County records and business were not transferred from Auburn until 1868 when Baker people went to Auburn, got the records and hauled them to Baker City in a wagon. Raymond (1870) indicated that about 5,000 acres of Baker County land had been improved for farming prior to his visit in 1869.

Baker City Opera House, built in 1889. The name was later changed to the Clarick. The building burned Nov. 12, 1937.

Virtue Mine crew.

*Virtue Mine
(Note three
children in lower
middle of photo)*

*Closer view of the Virtue
Mine. The reason for
building mills on a hill
slope: gravity helps move
the ore through the
crushing, grinding, and
concentrating stages of
the milling process.*

Virtue District

The Virtue district is centered about seven air miles east of Baker City. Most of the mines and prospects are in the arid low rolling hills surrounding Virtue Flat, a sage covered depression extending 8 miles east and west and 2 miles north and south. Water is scarce, Ruckels Creek near the east edge of the district being the only stream. The National Historic Oregon Trail Interpretive Center on the crest of Flagstaff Hill is a major tourist attraction. The Old Oregon Trail and State Highway 86 cross the district. Highway 86 is the initial leg of the Hells Canyon Scenic Byway.

Virtue Flat is underlain by Tertiary lake bed sedimentary deposits and younger alluvial deposits. Ancient ocean floor sedimentary and volcanic rocks and rocks representing an intrusive gabbro-diorite complex underlie the low hills rimming the flat. The sedimentary rocks, mostly fine grained silicic argillite and chert, occupy the southern part of the district.They locally contain Permian and Triassic radiolaria (microscopic marine fossils) according to a graduate student dissertation. A small exposure of Jurassic-Cretaceous granitic rock is cut by Highway 86 along the downgrade into Baker Valley. In parts of the area these ancient rocks are covered by Miocene basalt flows. The Oregon Trail Interpretive Center building is underlain by a small exposure of the basalt flows. Rocks of the gabbro-diorite complex underlie the basalt and are exposed in road cuts east of the parking lot and along the interpretive trails and roads on the slopes surrounding the center and in road cuts along Highway 86 east of the center.

Brooks and Ramp list 14 lode mines and prospects in the district. Lode mine production from the district totals more than $3,274,000, most of it from the Virtue ($2,200,000), White Swan ($724,000), Emma ($250,000), and Flagstaff ($100,000) mines. Smaller producers include the Rachel, Uncle Dan, Friday, and Hidden Treasure mines. Lode mines in the district are in metamorphosed gabbro and diorite, mafic volcanic rocks and fine grained silicic.

Virtue Mine

Virtue Mine, northeast Oregon's first and one of its richest lode gold mines, is located about a mile west and south of the Oregon Trail and about 3.6 miles south of the Oregon Trail Interpretative Center on Flagstaff Hill. Thousands of Oregon Trail emigrants had passed within a mile of the deposit before it was found in 1863 and began producing gold in 1864. It was found by placer miners, including Philip Waggy, who followed gold fragments uphill to their source. The gravel-filled gulches leading up to the veins are said to have yielded considerable placer gold. The gold-bearing veins of the Virtue Mine were found by W. H. Rockfellow and William C.Wills. U. S. Land Office records contain the notice of location of six quartz claims covering exposures of the veins filed August 22, 1863, by five individuals: Wm. C. Wills, A. G. Rockfellow, W. H. Rockfellow, Stephen Longfellow, and Janus A. Pinney. Five of the claims were located by right of preemption and one by right of discovery. The property was called the Union Quartz Lead. Each claim was 250 feet long and thus together covered 1,500 feet of the vein.

W. H. Rockfellow was a freight line operator and part time prospector, who in early 1863 was granted a contract to carry U. S. mail between Walla Walla, Auburn, and Boise Basin (Patera, p.13). Following discovery of the Virtue vein, Rockfellow sold his freght business to Wells Fargo &Company, effective the first of October, 1863.

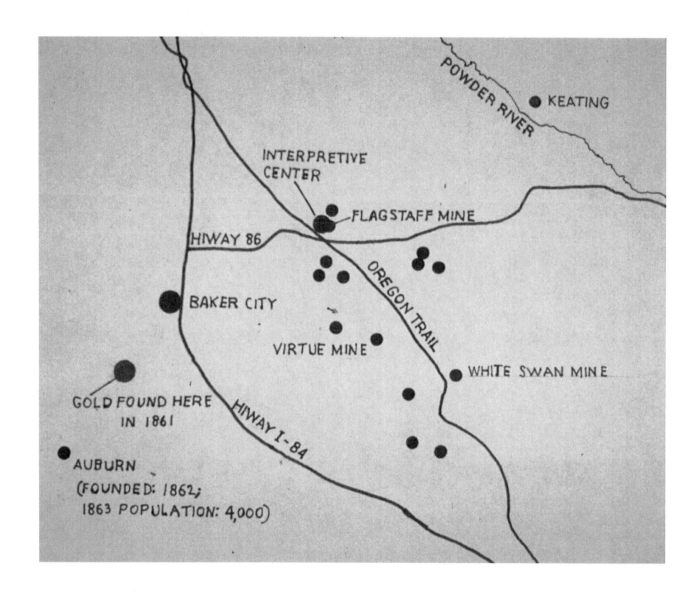

Virtue District index map.
Virtue Mine was the first lode mine in eastern Oregon.
Mining began in late 1863 or early 1864.

In 1864, Colonel J. S. Ruckel sold his interest in the Oregon Portage Railway at Cascade Locks and moved to Baker City. He soon acquired an interest in the Virtue Mine and built a stamp mill in Baker City to extract gold from the ore from the mine. The mill was built near Powder River seven miles from the mine because a lot of water was needed to power the mill and there was none at the mine. Water was obtained from a ditch connecting with the Powder River. The mill was one of the first structures in future Baker City. A twenty-stamp mill was erected at the mine about 1874 after water to run the mill was found in the mine, thus avoiding the seven-mile wagon journey into Baker City. Water in the lower parts of the mine was warm, making working conditions uncomfortable for the miners.

Lindgren (1901, pp. 722-723) said the veins of the Virtue Mine were discovered in 1864 by W. H. Rockfellow and a Mr. Wills. For the next ten years the mine was known as the Ruckel or Union Mine and it was very actively worked. Between 1871 and 1878, it was worked almost continuously, largely by A. H. Brown and J. W. Virtue. About 1874, it was sold to Grayson & Company of San Francisco, who worked it in a more or less satisfactory way until 1884. It was then idle until 1893 when work was resumed and continued until 1898 with excellent results. After a short period of idleness the mine was sold to the Consolidated Virtue Mine Co. of Montreal, Canada, which owned the adjoining Collateral Mine. The upper parts of the mine were worked for a short time and the mine was again closed August 1, 1899. The mine has not been worked since then, except for a brief interval in 1907 when a little ore was extracted above the drainage level and about $1,500 was a obtained from ore on the dump. The total production has been about $2,200,000.

Three Periods of Production

There were three periods of production, 1864-1884; 1893-1899;1906-1907. Ownership changed hands several times. James W. Virtue, a prominent Baker City citizen, was part owner in 1868 - 1872 (Dielman, 2004). He was Baker County Sheriff at the time (1866-1870) and later started the first bank in Baker City in 1870. The mine produced about $2,200,000 in gold before its underground workings were closed and allowed to fill with water in 1907.

The gold was found to be in a nearly vertical tabular-shaped quartz vein that ranged from a few inches to 12 feet thick, averaging about 14 inches thick. The ore body had a maximum length of 1200 feet and depth of 800 feet. The ore averaged 0.5 to one ounce of gold per ton but there was some high grade; one little pocket of ore contained $40,000 worth of gold; one chunk weighing 90 pounds gave mint returns of $14,000, equal to 677 ounces of gold at $20.67 per ounce. To dig out the gold-bearing vein, miners sank a shaft 800 feet deep and from it drove horizontal tunnels at 100-foot intervals. About 10,000 feet of horizontal tunnel gave access to the vein.

The Virtue Mine employed 20 Chinese and 12 white men in 1872 and was the first lode mine north of California to employ Chinese as underground miners. The Chinese were paid half as much as the white men (Raymond, 1873, p. 212; Wegars, 1995, p. 55).The reason for building mills on a hill slope: gravity helps move ore through the crushing, grinding, and concentrating stages of the milling process. In later years Harvey and George Gardner took a lot of specimen gold from small quartz veins in the slope southeast of the Virtue Mine. Some of the specimens are in the gold display at U. S. National Bank in Baker City. They processed some gold-bearing quartz in a small gravity mill located at their home. The Gardner brothers divided their time between truck gardening on an acreage on Salmon Creek and gold mining.

Flagstaff Mine Buildings

Flagstaff Cyanide vats

Flagstaff Crew

White Swan Mine

White Swan Band

Uncle Dan Mine

Uncle Dan Mine, southern region of Virtue District. Tailing piles and mine shafts are about all that remain of the mine.

Flagstaff

Dumps of old tailings from the Flagstaff Mine are visible along the road about 300 yards east of the Oregon Trail Interpretive Center. If the buildings were still standing you could see them from the front patio of the Center. This old mine included a shaft 760 feet deep and about 6000 feet of tunnel. The mine had a multitude of different owners all of whom failed to keep the mine operating for more than a few months at a time. Records indicate that the mine produced about $90,000 in1897 and $32,000 in 1898 (Oman). The Skovlins (2001) say that George McCarty discovered the Flagstaff deposit, 6 miles northeast of Baker City in 1895. "He and three adjacent claim holders were able to sell the Flagstaff Mine for $51,000 ($1,039,884 in today's dollars) (p. 278). The mine developed three well-defined quartz veins and had 5,000 feet of workings by 1900 and 6,000 ft by 1933 (Oman). The Baker *Morning Democrat* reported: "Flagstaff has 6 claims, 728 foot inclined shaft, over 4,000 feet of development work. Three parallel veins vary from 3 to 6 feet thick. Ore averages $15 per ton; 10-stamp mill is on the ground but a cyanide plant is needed. The mining world was astonished by the high grade free-milling ore the mine turned out."

White Swan Mine

The White Swan Mine was operated during 1890-1897, 1916, and 1935-1937. Lorain (1938) gives a flow sheet of the mill used in 1935-1937. Underground development includes a 300-foot shaft with 4 levels totalling 2,000 feet. According to Gilluly (1933) the total production of the mine was $724,000. Swartley (1914, p.131) says, "The mine was worked successfully in the 1880s and was idle from 1897 to about 1900 when Letson Balliet promoted this and other mines with a brass band and other similar features until 1903 when Federal government stopped his operations. Pre-1916 production estimated as not less than $200,000." The host rock is argillite cut by several diorite dikes. There are many small veins in the vicinity, and in some, chimneys of coarse gold have been found, although none of large amount.

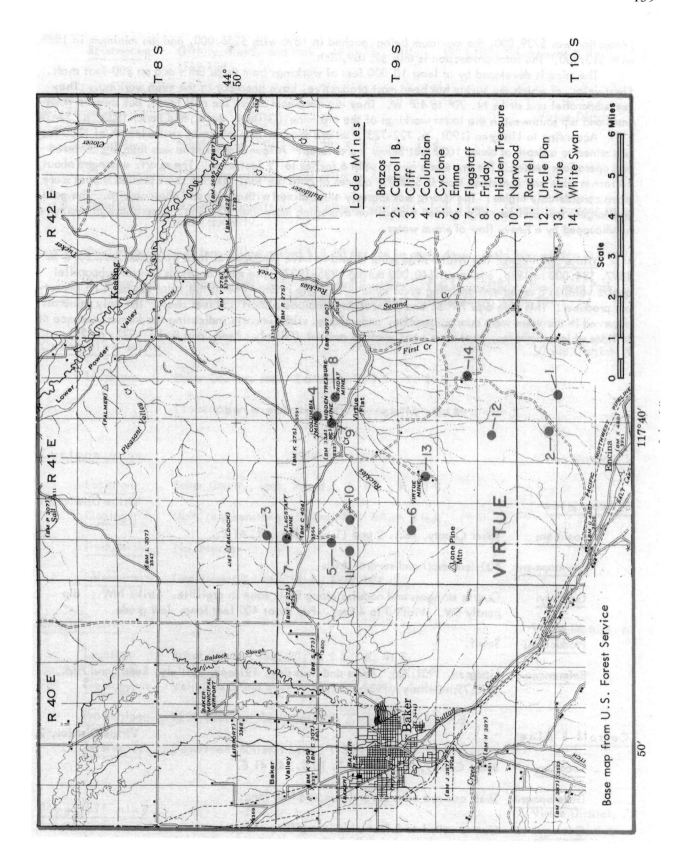

Lode Mines

1. Brazos
2. Carroll B.
3. Cliff
4. Columbian
5. Cyclone
6. Emma
7. Flagstaff
8. Friday
9. Hidden Treasure
10. Norwood
11. Rachel
12. Uncle Dan
13. Virtue
14. White Swan

Base map from U.S. Forest Service

Index Map Virtue Mining District

Eagle Creek, Sparta, and Keating Districts

These districts are in the foothills of the Wallowa Mountains northeast of Baker City. Gold quartz veins occur in sandstones, shales, and greenstones in Eagle Creek and Sanger districts and albite granite, diorite, and gabbro in Sparta District. Copper-and gold-bearing veins and replacement bodies have formed along shear zones in greenstone in the Keating District. Deposits probably are related to the Wallowa batholith. Most of the lode mine production came from the Sanger Mine. Small output came from the Mother Lode copper mine, and from the Macy, Basin, Gem, Dolly Varden, East Eagle, and other mines. Lode production: 95,000-130,000 ounces of gold. Placer mining in gulches leading up to the Sanger Mine produced $500,000 prior to 1901. Sparta and Eagle Creek placers are said to have been very rich.

Eagle Creek District

Eagle Creek District includes the upper drainage of Eagle Creek and the adjoining area on the Powder River slope northeast of Keating that is drained by Clover, Balm, and Goose creeks. Roads enter the district from Sparta, Keating, and Medical Springs. Elevations at the mines range from 3,500 to 7,000 feet. Most of the area is timbered and there are several permanent streams.

Pre-Tertiary rocks exposed in the district include greenstones, tuffs, and related volcaniclastic sedimentary rocks of the Clover Creek Greenstone; limestone of the Martin Bridge Formation; and sand-stones, mudstones, and shales of the Hurwal formation. Granitic rocks of the Wallowa Batholith underlie the northern part of the area. A large part of the district is blanketed by Tertiary basalt. The Sparta Quadrangle geologic map (Prostka, 1963) covers most of the district.

Lode-gold production from Eagle Creek district is dominated by the Sanger Mine, whose output has been estimated at $1,500,000. The Mother Lode copper mine produced a limited amount of gold as well as copper during 1935-1938. Production from other lode deposits in the Eagle Creek district has been small. Some of the better known prospects are the Basin, East Eagle, Amalgamated, Lily White, and Dolly Varden mines.

Eagle Creek Placers

Lindgren (1901) said, "The Eagle Creek Placers have been worked ever since the late 1860s and each season some placer mining is done. All along Eagle Creek there are benches of heavy gravel up to 100 feet above the stream. These benches have been worked to some degree from below the mouth of Paddy Creek to a few miles up stream above the mouth of East Eagle Creek. Placer mines are found on both upper and lower Paddy Creek." Press reports of June, 1916, state that 30 men were at work constructing a large ditch to carry water for hydraulic purposes (Swartley, 16:88).

Sanger Mine

Sanger Mine, one of the first lode mines developed in eastern Oregon, is located on a branch of Goose Creek near the top of the Powder River-Eagle Creek divide at about 4000 feet elevation.

Map showing location of mines in northeastern part of gold belt

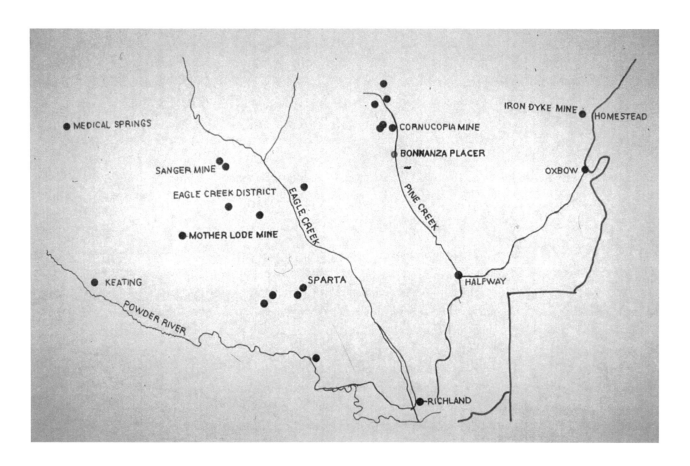

Goose Creek drains into Powder River at the lower end of Keating Valley. The Sanger mine area was first called Hogum. Some say that name alluded to the perceived stinginess of the early miners in the district who tried to prevent late comers from locating claims in the area. Others say the name honored one of the first prospectors to find gold in the area. It was later named Augusta in honor of the daughter of W.H. Packwood. She was the first unmarried woman to live in the district. Finally, it was named Sanger, honoring the manager and part owner of the mine during its most productive years.

The property is presently owned by William Wendt, grandson of James K. Romig, who was part of a group of investors who acquired the mine in 1903. In 1946 after his discharge from military service during World War II. Wendt attended college on the GI Bill, then spent a long career employed as metallurgist for several different companies. He is now retired and living in his hometown, Baker City. The mine is his summer home. At one time the Sanger property included 400 acres of patented mining claims with 300 acres along Eagle Creek originally, but reduced to 74 acres in recent years. The following discussion of the mine is based on information from Lindgren (1901, pp.738-739) and unpublished reports in DOGAMI mine files by Charles P. Berkey (undated) and N. S. Wagner (November 31, 1967) and conversations with William Wendt.

Placer mining in gulches leading up to the Sanger Mine reportedly produced more than $500,000 in gold (Lindgren 1901, pp. 738-739) The principal vein, called the Summit Lode, was discovered in 1870 and was actively worked in succeeding years (Lindgren). Early operators were Colonel E. E. Clough and C. H. Duncan. In 1874 the production was $60,000 on ore yielding $16 in gold per ton. Initially, ore was milled in a single-bed arrastra. The arrastra was replaced about 1865 by a 5-stamp mill brought from San Francisco. It was located near where Wendt's cabin is today. Clough disliked the stamp mill and replaced it with a large double-bed arrastra. Part of the ore treated in the stamp mills in the early days was gold-rich quartz fragments found in gulches below Sanger Mine. Wendt continues to produce small amounts of gold from such sources in summer months using a small gravity separation mill. The total production to 1887 is unknown, though probably small. The Knight claim was relocated (record filed on March 28, 1887) by Clough and Duncan.

A ten-stamp mill was built in 1887 by C. M. Sanger. Mint reports say the mine produced $813,000 in the years 1889-1892. Records for succeding years are not available but production reportedly continued until 1897 using the same management, crew strength, and milling process. Thus it has been assumed that the 1892-1897 production was about the same as that in 1889-1892. Total production has been estimated at more than $1,500,000 (Holland, 1996, p.227).

The rocks at the Sanger Mine are dark colored marine mudstone and shale of the Upper Triassic Hurwal Formation. Wall rocks contain a little pyrite near the veins. The Summit Vein strikes nearly due east, dips 30 degrees north and has been worked to dip depth of 400 feet from several adits and an inclined shaft. An old map dated January 1, 1901, indicates that drifting was done on at least two other veins or fault zones, one paralleling the Summit Vein and the other crossing it at nearly right angles. Wendt believes that the cross vein is the Packwood vein and that the $60,000 production in 1874 was taken from that vein by Colonel Clough. The Packwood, Golden Eagle, Knight, and Big veins are exposed on the surface. The Big Vein at the head of Fir Gulch may have been the major source of the rich placers on Fir Gulch. The vein has not been developed. Berkey said it should be explored. He also thought the Knight Vein appeared promising on the surface.

The ore shoot in the upper stopes of the Summit Vein was 600 feet long, about 15 inches wide, and averaged $20 to $25 a ton in gold; below the zone of oxidation the vein widened to between 2 and 4 feet and the value dropped to $12 a ton. The gangue was coarse quartz with a little calcite and about 3 percent sulfides, mostly pyrite with a little sphalerite and galena. Much of the gold was free of sulfides. In its easterly extension on all levels the vein bends in a broad curve to the south and appears to blend with the strike of the the host rocks losing its characteristic size and value. Toward the west the vein has been offset by faulting, at which point mining ceased. W.J. Townley of Union was mine superintendant in the 1880s.

The mine was inactive in 1897-1900 due to the illness and ensuing death of Mr. Sanger. In 1900, the mine was acquired by the Sanger Development Company headed by J. K. Romig, grandfather of the present owner, William Wendt. In an unpublished report written about 1910 titled *The Sanger Mine*, Professor Charles P. Berkey PhD, University of Minnesota, said that the development company spent $80,000 on work that included sinking the main shaft 300 feet below the old workings and prospecting new ground, plus enlarging the property, settling litigations, and perfecting equipment. Good ore was reportedly found in the shaft extension. Based on the exploration results, Romig decided to bring electricity to the mine and mill and resume mine operations.

Blue Mountain American newspaper (January 2, 2004) reported the Sanger Mine owner's plans (mainly J.K.Romig's) to build a 3,000 HP transmission plant on Eagle Creek. Holland (1996) says Eagle River Electric Power Company was formed with plans to build an 800 KW power plant and 30 miles of transmission line to furnish power to the Sanger, Mother Lode and Virtue mines and the City of Baker City. A franchise to furnish power to Baker City was obtained. The power plant and transmission lines were built in 1911-12 and operations were started and carried on until December 31, 1913, when a snow slide destroyed a 3,000 foot section of the canal that furnished water to turn the plant's pelton wheel. Bill Wendt told me that the ditch was repaired and power production resumed for a short time but the ditch failed again. This led to cancellation of the contract with Baker City and eventual abandonment of the power project.

Old cabin at Sanger, courtesy of Bill Wendt.

Sanger Boarding House.

Sanger Mine mill and smaller buildings.

Sanger mill vanner room

Sanger Mine crew in front of the boarding house.

Sparta Store, built in 1872 by brothers Sigmund and Seligmann Heilner.

Amalgamated Mine

The Amalgamated Mine was owned and the assessment work maintained by Nadie Strayer of Baker for over 30 years until her death in 1991. She leased or optioned it several times to different companies and individuals but none did substantial amounts of development or exploration work. Nadie was the daughter of Oregon State Senator Strayer, who was instrumental in the formation of the Oregon Department of Geology and Mineral Industries.

Dolly Varden

The Dolly Varden Mine recorded pre-1900 production of $115,000 in gold from surface ore, as reported by Lindgren (1901). Several major mining firms have investigated the prospect at various times in recent decades (pre-1990) and, overall, a considerable amount of surface and drill sampling has been done without success in finding new ore.

Sparta District

The Sparta District encompasses a small area including part of the divide between Eagle Creek and Powder River in the vicinity of Sparta, a ghost town about 40 miles by road east of Baker City. Elevations range from about 2,300 feet on Powder River along the southern edge of the district to 4,944 feet at the top of Sparta Butte in the northern part. Timber is absent on the Powder River slope of the divide but plentiful to the north. The host rocks of the district are albite granite and quartz diorite of Early Triassic age (Prostka, 1962). The intrusive rocks are sheared and deeply decomposed. Patches of Cenozoic basaltic lava flows, silicic tuffs, and lake and stream sedimentary deposits cover the old rocks.

The ghost town of Sparta had a succession of different names in its early days. It was named Kooster in 1863, then Eagle City, then Gem Town, then Sparta. The first Post Office in the area was established on August 7, 1871, at Gem Town a village of about 250 people located near the Gem Mine. The Post Office was moved to Sparta October 29, 1872. The townsite had been laid out January 8, 1871, by William H. Packwood, E. P. Cranston, I. B. Bowen, and C. M. Foster. The name was selected by Packwood for his hometown, Sparta, Illinois. Packwood and others were preparing to build the Sparta Ditch to assist placer mining at that time.

The Sparta Mining District was noted mainly for its placers, principally those along Shanghai Gulch and adjacent drainages. Gold was discovered in Shanghai Gulch, a tributary of Eagle Creek, in 1863 by Squire Morris and Neales Donnelly (Makinson, 1980, p. 2; Steeves, 1984, pp. 69, 73). The Sparta Ditch, completed in 1873, furnished water for working these placers.

In her book, *Gold, Jade, and Elegance*, Helen Rand quotes William Packwood as saying that while the Sparta Ditch was being built there were about 500 white men and 1,000 Chinese living in Sparta. He said, "You could smell the opium a mile away"(1974, p. 47). Smoking opium was one of the few comforts in the hard working lives of the Chinese so far from their homes and families. There were few Chinese women in the gold camps.

The several quartz veins that have been developed in the district are small and nonpersistent,

Gem Mine near Sparta.

Sanger Mine. Dan Hayes, foreman, ca. 1894, picking loose rock from the back and walls of a stope.

but contained pockets of rich gold ore. Total lode production is believed to be small. Lindgren's figure of $677,000 for the four years 1889-1892 is said by local historians to be greatly exaggerated.

.

Macy Mine

The Macy Mine in Maiden Gulch, a quarter of a mile above Powder River and Oregon Highway 86, was discovered in 1920. Intermittent operations have produced in the neighborhood of $90,000. About 2,000 feet of development work has been done, mainly from adit levels. Early work was mapped by Gilluly, Reed, and Park (1933, p. 61). The workings explore several small quartz veins of diverse trend, some of which intersect. The veins range in width from about an inch to 4 feet, and consist chiefly of quartz with a little calcite, sericite, and chlorite. Ore minerals are pyrite, sphalerite, and free gold. Ore shoots were small and irregular. Stope widths averaged 1 to 12 feet. Kenneth Grabner took out much of the $90,000. Grabner was one of the best go-it-alone prospectors I've known. He told me he took some gold out of the Flagstaff, Hidden Treasure, and Record mines as well as the Macy.

The Macys are a pioneer family. I knew only Clyde. He came into the DOGAMI office and visited with me many times during my first years with the Department. At that time, because of his age he did little more than talk about prospecting. He said he worked in the Macy mine as a young man. He delighted in showing people his "gold nuggets" which were authentic-looking fakes made from brass welding rod.

Gem Mine

Probably the most extensive underground development is at the Gem Mine where, according to Lorain (1938, p. 33), there is an inclined shaft 550 feet deep from which short drifts have been turned on eight different levels. The vein strikes north, dips 300 to 400 east, and ranges from 1 to 4 feet in width between sharply defined walls. It consists of crushed and altered albite granite with streaks and lenses of quartz as much as 2 feet wide. The ore ordinarily consists of coarse quartz containing free gold with pyrite and sphalerite .

Crystal Palace Mine

At the Crystal Palace Mine, about 2,000 feet of workings develop a curving vein which strikes from N. 30 W. to N. 60 E. and dips about 25 E. The vein consists of pyrite, arsenopyrite, and free gold in a gangue of quartz and minor sericite, chlorite, and ankerite.

Above: Poorman Mine on Balm Creek, Keating District.

Below: The Burkemont prospect was located and developed to its present state prior to 1900. Soil sampling was done by DOGAMI in 1960 (Koch and Bowen, 1960). Two exploration diamond drill holes were drilled by Kennecott Copper Company in the early 1960's.

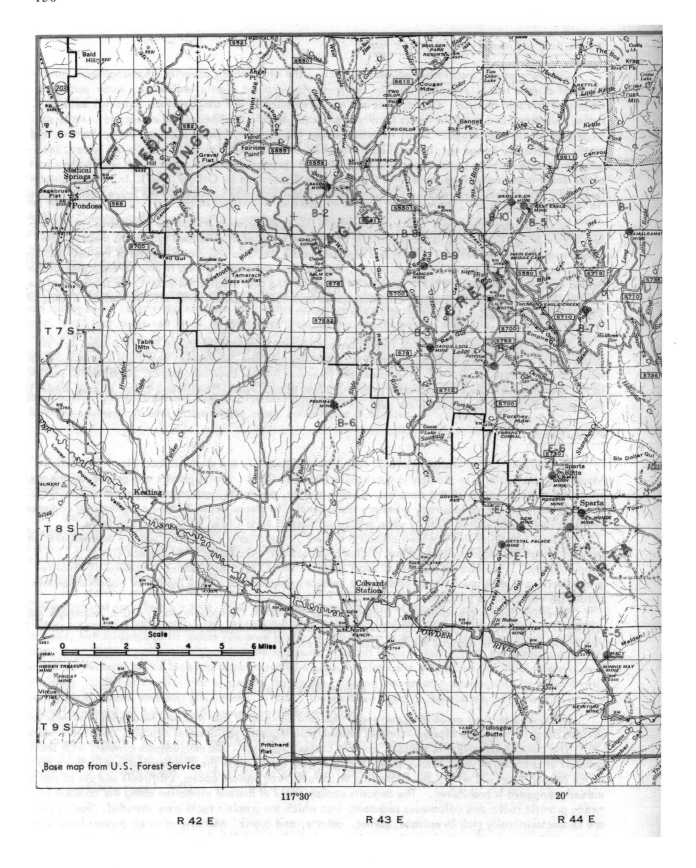

Index Map of Sparta and Medical Springs Districts

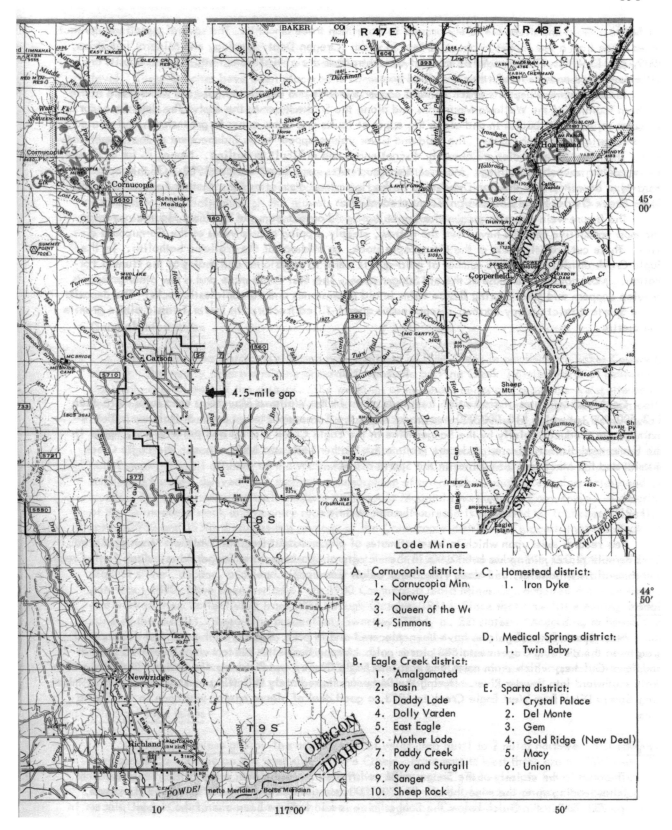

4.5-mile gap

Lode Mines

A. Cornucopia district:
1. Cornucopia Min...
2. Norway
3. Queen of the We...
4. Simmons

B. Eagle Creek district:
1. Amalgamated
2. Basin
3. Daddy Lode
4. Dolly Varden
5. East Eagle
6. Mother Lode
7. Paddy Creek
8. Roy and Sturgill
9. Sanger
10. Sheep Rock

C. Homestead district:
1. Iron Dyke

D. Medical Springs district:
1. Twin Baby

E. Sparta district:
1. Crystal Palace
2. Del Monte
3. Gem
4. Gold Ridge (New Deal)
5. Macy
6. Union

Index map of Cornucopia, Eagle, and Homestead Districts

Cornucopia District

Cornucopia 1884

Cornucopia mill vanners and concentrator room.

Cornucopia portal of Coulter Adit, boarded over.

Cornucopia Mine

Ten miles north of Halfway was Oregon's most productive gold mine. Estimates of total output range from $10,000,000 to $17,000,000 in gold and by-products: silver, copper, lead, and zinc.

Cornucopia town and mines, 1915

The miners dug gold ore from two veins about 1,500 feet apart called the Union-Companion and Last Chance veins. Mine development began about 1880-1884, and included about 36 miles of underground workings. Nineteen levels were driven. The three adits shown (horizontal accessway driven from the surface) at elevations of 4800, 5800 and 6910 feet gave access to different parts of the veins. The underground workings were interconnected from the top to the bottom of the mine, a vertical distance of 2,150 feet.

The mine employed 176 workers in 1900. In 1902 the town of Cornucopia had two hotels, two general stores, two livery stables, along with the appropriate number of meat markets, bakeries, barber shops, saloons, dance halls and other businesses of a small mining town. Population of the town in 1940 was about 350. The town died quickly after the mine was closed in 1941. Sometimes the snow got really deep in Cornucopia. Twelve to 15 feet of snow is not uncommon for the area. The mines are in country so steep and snow so deep that avalanches destroyed many mine structures and killed or injured several people.

Ore was transported from mine to mill by trams. The Last Chance tram was about a mile long and Queen of west one-quarter mile long says Carmellita Holland. In 1939 160-175 tons of ore per day were milled and 2 or 3 tons of concentrates were trucked to Robinette and from there shipped by rail to smelter at Tacoma.

Alonzo G. Simmons is said to have been among the first prospectors who discovered the gold quartz veins that started the lode gold mining rush to the Cornucopia area in 1884. The Simmons Mine and Simmons Mountain, located across Pine Creek Canyon from Cornucopia, were named in his honor.

Cornucopia and the Cornucopia Mine

History of Cornucopia and of mine employment is based on information contained in unpublished reports and clippings from various issues of Oregon Mining Review magazine and *The Record-Courier* newspaper housed in the mine files of the Oregon Department of Geology and Mineral Industries (DOGAMI). Information about the mines is from reports published by DOGAMI and its predecessor, the Oregon Bureau of Mines, and private reports in DOGAMI files.

Above: Cornucopia Crew on electric tram

Below: Drilling contest in Cornucopia. One man holds the drill steel while his partner hits it with a sledge hammer.

Cornucopia, located on the west bank of Pine Creek 10 miles north of Halfway, Oregon, was born in the early 1880s. It became a mining boomtown in 1885 when prospectors began flocking to the area, having heard that rich gold veins had been found in the granite mountains to the north. The name Cornucopia, meaning "horn of plenty," was suggested by a group of prospectors from Cornucopia, Nevada. Many gold veins were found in succeeding years and heralded by such names as Red Jacket, Robert Emmett, Mayflower, Queen of the West, Last Chance and Union-Companion. The area never became another Virginia City, Nevada, as some early prospectors had speculated was sure to happen. Ore from upper oxidized parts of some veins was quite rich -- rich enough to return a sizeable profit after having been put in bags, hauled to Baker, first by packhorses, later by wagon, and shipped by rail to the Tacoma smelter. Mine employment in the Cornucopia district remained an important part of Baker County's economy until the beginning of World War II. Cornucopia post office was established December 7, 1885, and closed in June 1942.

The Cornucopia Mine worked two veins, the Union-Companion and the Last Chance. The principal outcrops of the Union-Companion and Last Chance veins are at elevations of 6,100 feet and 7,000 feet respectively on the rugged west wall of Pine Creek Canyon. The veins are approximately parallel, sheet-like bodies ranging from 2 to 25 feet wide dipping 45 degrees westward toward the core of the mountain. They vary from 1,500 to 2,500 feet apart horizontally. After 1920, Union-Companion and Last Chance were worked concurrently as parts of the Cornucopia Mine.

The mine's main productive periods were 1907-1927 and 1930-1941. Production prior to 1903 has been estimated at $1,008,000. Recorded output during 1903-1941 totals 272,777 ounces of gold and 1,088,051 ounces of silver. During the life of the mine, gold was valued at $20.67 per troy ounce prior to 1934 and $35 after 1934. The 1903-1941 production would be worth about $163,666,200 at today's prices of around $600 per troy ounce. (One troy ounce equals about 1.1 avoirdupois ounce).

The mine was closed in October 1941 prior to U.S. entry into World War II. Closure occurred largely because developed ore was depleted and mining and development costs were increasing rapidly due to the war in Europe. Since the war, there have been various ill-fated attempts to reactivate the mine but no further production. Little remains of the town except old dilapidated buildings and a few summer cabins.

The number of workers employed in the mining and milling operations ranged from 175 in 1936 to 350 in 1940. This was during the mine's peak period of production and development. Monthly pay per employee in 1936 averaged about $90. During the 1936-1941 era, much of the mining was done by contract miners who were paid according to the amount of rock they had drilled, blasted, and loaded on ore cars for transport out of the mine during the month.

By the time mining ended in 1941 the mountain had been honeycombed by about 36 miles of underground workings. As mentioned, there were three main entries to the mine: The Coulter adit at 4,805 feet elevation near the level of Pine Creek at the north edge of the old townsite of Cornucopia is the lowest level adit (see photo at the top of page 152). The Coulter adit was the main haulageway during the last phase of mining in 1936-1941; the Clark level adit located near the head of Fall Creek, 985 feet above and 1½ miles northwest of the old townsite, gave access for earlier work on both the Union-Companion and Last Chance veins; the Last Chance Adit (also known as the Lawrence Adit),

Above: Last Chance crew

Left: Last Chance Road

Right: Last Chance tram--2 buckets

Left: Last Chance road and famous tree.

Right" Last Chance mill and tram line. Top of mill visible at bottom; tram lines barely visible against mountain slope.

the highest adit level, at 6910 feet elevation and 0.8 mile north of the Clark level adit, was the only access to the Last Chance vein prior to about 1920. The workings became interconnected by raises and shafts as mining progressed so that eventually access to all 19 levels of the mine between the Coulter level (4,805 feet) and the Lawrence level (6,910 feet) was possible inside the mountain.

Mine development began in the mid-1880s but progressed slowly because of the high, rugged, and snowy terrane and long distance to rail transportation. At least three small mills were built but all proved inefficient. The best of them, a 20-stamp mill and chlorination plant, placed in operation in 1896 extracted only about 65 percent of the values contained in the ore. Production became steady and profitable after Cornucopia Mines Company took over operation of the Union-Companion Mine and built and began operating a well-devised cyanide plant adjacent to the Clark adit in early 1913. The process which included fine grinding (80 percent through a 200-mesh screen) and cyanidation of the finely ground ore in a large vat increased recovery to 90 percent.

The success of the Cornucopia Mines Company operation of the Union-Companion Mine fostered organization of the Baker Mines Company, which leased and took over development and mining of the Last Chance Vein in late 1913. The company was formed by major stockholders of the Cornucopia Mines Company and was named for Last Chance Mine manager, John M. Baker. A 20-stamp mill and cyanide plant was built on the East Fork of Pine Creek north of Cornucopia and began operating in late October 1914. An aerial tram was built and used to transport ore from the Lawrence adit to the mill, a slope distance of 5,500 feet and vertical distance of 1,675 feet. Stella Grubbe is quoted as saying that in 1920 she rode one of the tram buckets from mill to mine three days before it broke and was never used again. One of the buckets "run away down the line and they braked it too fast and snapped the cable" *(Pine Valley Echo,* vol. II, p. 11).

Prior to 1936 the Union-Companion vein was mined by way of the Clark adit crosscut and the ore was treated in the Union mill. Most of the ore-bearing zone was below the adit level. Shafts were sunk and the ore was blasted from stopes in the vein then hoisted to the adit level and trammed to the mill. About 1920, costs had become too high for that type of mining and work on the Union vein was discontinued. Underground connections were made with the Last Chance vein and ore from that vein was mined from stopes above the adit level and treated in the Union mill until about 1929 when rising costs forced cessation of both mine and mill operations. Later, a new company, Cornucopia Gold Mines, Inc., reopened the property and in 1935-1936 drove the Coulter adit crosscut and began mining the Union vein below the old workings. The crosscut did not reach the Last Chance vein.

A 250-tons-per-day flotation mill was built near the adit portal and operated almost continuously until the mine was closed permanently in October 1941. Concentrates, consisting of sulfide minerals, gold and silver extracted from the ore by the mill, were trucked to Robinette and from there shipped by railroad to the Tacoma Smelter.

Robinette was a small town on the bank of Snake River about a mile above the mouth of Powder River below Richland. The town site was laid out by Edward Robinette in October 1908. It and the railroad bed were inundated by Brownlee Reservoir in 1958.

The veins are mainly quartz. In most places they are in a type of intrusive rock called granodiorite. Ore minerals are native gold and silver occurring as very fine particles in pyrite and other sulfide

Union Mine and Mill area

*Union Mine
Mill*

*Dinnertime for the
Union Mine Crew*

minerals. Some of the ore contained free gold and gold and silver telluride minerals, especially in the upper levels of the mines. The ore contained about 5 times more silver than gold but the gold was far more valuable due to price differences.

UNC acquired the property, comprised of about 1,000 acres of patented mining claims, in 1981. Work by this company included reopening of the Coulter and Clark level adits and investigation of old workings on the Union-Companion vein below the Coulter level where very little mining had been done. Some sampling was done of the Last Chance vein below the Clark adit level. UNC stopped work in October 1982 due to financial problems and the mine has been offered for sale. All of the pre-1941 surface structures built on Cornucopia mine property have been dismantled and removed or burned.

What's in the future for the Cornucopia Mine? According to an unpublished report in DOGAMI files by H. Farrel Anderson, a mining engineer employed by the mine in 1940-41, the Union-Companion and Last Chance veins were exhausted of proven, ready-to-mine ore when the mine closed in 1941. The mine had an operating loss of about $77,000 for that year. He said both veins are likely to continue to considerable depth below existing workings and they probably would contain ore of about the same quality as that found in the areas already mined. But, given the great increases in the costs of mine and mill construction and operation it is not likely that ore of such quality could be developed, mined and milled at a profit even though the price of gold is now many times its value in 1941.

The Cornucopia Mining Company name was used in a stock swindle in the 1950s. According to newspaper accounts of the time, Earl Belle gained control of the company in 1957 and used the company name in building a $5.5 million paper empire by issuing new shares and swapping them for controlling stock in several other small companies. Belle's empire collapsed in 1958. The FBI charged him with 31 counts of fraud. He fled to Brazil in 1958 with about $1,000,000, most of it in unsecured loans from banks eager to loan money to the "boy wizard" on the basis of his vast holdings. The mine property sold for $51,000 in bankruptcy court in 1958. The Security and Exchange Commission ordered delisting of Cornucopia stock in 1960.

Last Chance Mine

The buildings shown here are perched on a ridge top at about 6,910 feet elevation. They housed the Last Chance Mine crew and equipment maintenance shops at the uppermost adit entry to the Last Chance vein of the Cornucopia Mine.

An aerial tram was used to transport ore from the mine adit to the mill a little over a mile away down this very steep mountainside. The tram was abandoned about 1920 and ore from the Last Chance vein was drawn down inside the mountain to the Union adit and concentrated at the Union Mill (Sybil Smith, *Pine Valley Vignettes*, 1996). Last Chance buildings burned in 1922 said John Zimmerman.

Last Chance road. Some mine roads in the early days were very primitive and certainly would not pass today's worker safety standards.

Last Chance Mine's Baker Mill

Last Chance in Snow

*Last Chance
Mine*

Above: Some houses almost buried in deep Cornucopia snow. Ca. 1915.

Below: Digging out from an Avalanche at Cornucopia.

For its proficient reclamation at its Pine Creek operations, Bonnanza Mining Company was awarded DOGAMI's 1991 Operator of the Year Award for eastern Oregon. This was formerly a pit for placer operations.

Bonnanza Placer

The following is from notes provided by Thomas Bonn.

Bonnanza Mining, Inc., began placer mining the gravel of Pine Creek about three miles below Cornucopia in 1986. The treatment plant, consisting of standard gravity equipment, including two trommel screens, vibrating sluice, nugget trap, and Nelson concentrator mounted on a truck bed handled 65 to 70 yards of gravel per hour. The gravel was hauled to the plant in 35-ton dump trucks, stockpiled and later fed to the plant by hydraulic excavator. The plant was operated about eight months per year, three 8-hour shifts per day, six days per week. The pit ran two 10-hour shifts per day. Thirty people were employed. Wages normally ranged between $7.00 and $13.00 per hour. Stripping and some reclamation work was done during early winter and late spring when freezing weather prevented operation of the plant. Reclamation was concurrent with mining. Mined areas were back-filled to natural-looking, generally better-contoured condition than the original ground. Topsoil, which was stockpiled during mining was replaced and the soil was replanted with native plants and grasses. The restored ground was landscaped with rocks and downed trees carefully arranged to provide habitat for small animals and insects. By the end of 1989, about 20 acres had been mined and six acres had been reclaimed. Costs averaged about 50 cents per cubic yard for mining and $1,000 per acre for reclamation.

The operation was developed and managed for the first few years by Thomas Bonn. Pine Creek was well known to contain significant gold values before the Bonn operation but previous attempts at mining were largely unsuccessful because the stream channel is narrow and steep. Most of the values are on or near bed rock beneath up to 70 feet of gravel which contains many large boulders. During part of the mining season, Pine Creek contains a large volume of water which must be diverted and kept clear of mine waste. About 85 percent of the water was recirculated via the use of 6 hydroclones. The remaining 15 percent flowed into three settling ponds and from there was recirculated. The overburden was stripped away in benches using hydraulic excavators located on benches about 15 feet above the dump trucks being loaded. The overburden was dumped over the bedrock and large boulders left behind in worked-out portions of the pit; thus, reclamation was concurrent with mining.

Homestead Mining District

Homestead is the long-abandoned camp of the Iron Dyke Mine, Oregon's largest copper producer. The camp is located on an alluvial fan at the mouth of Iron Dyke Creek on the Oregon bank of Snake River about four miles north of Oxbow.

Parks and Swartley (1916) list 15 prospects in Oregon within a few miles of the camp, none of which is known to have produced a significant amount of copper or gold. Across Snake River in the Seven Devils mining district of Idaho there are several small mines that collectively produced about $1,000,000 in copper and by-product gold and silver prior to 1910 and one mine, the Copper Cliff, that produced 12,547,883 pounds of copper, 349,073 ounces of silver and 11 ounces of gold between 1972 and 1981. Copper deposits in the Seven Devils District occur in irregular, discontinuous bodies associated with garnet-bearing rock (tactite) along the margins of metamorphosed limestone and intrusive quartz diorite.

Iron Dyke Mine

The Iron Dyke Mine at Homestead produced large amounts of copper as well as gold. The deposit was discovered in 1897 by two brothers, Jake and Bert Vaughn, who owned a homestead at the present site of Oxbow Village and were running cattle in the Iron Dyke Mine area. The Vaughns were nephews of the infamous McCarty Brothers gang of outlaws (Skovlin and Skovlin, 2001). They named their homestead Copperfield which, a few years later, was sold to land speculators and became a town that served two large construction crews, one extending a spur of the Oregon Railway and Navigation Company (O.R. & N.) downriver from Huntington to Homestead and another building an electric power plant at the sharp bend in Snake River known as The Oxbow.

The railroad was completed in 1909 and the power plant in 1913. As residents moved away, Copperfield became known as the "baddest, bawdiest, most unlawful" town in Oregon and all the saloons, gambling halls and red light establishments were closed down in January, 1914, by a diminutive (104 pounds) but tough young lady named Fern Hobbs, secretary to the governor, supported by soldiers acting on orders from Oregon's Governor Oswald West. The town burned shortly afterward and never recovered. The Copperfield site became Oxbow Village when Idaho Power Company started construction of three power dams across Snake River in the 1950s – 1960s: Hells Canyon Dam, 20 miles below Homestead; and two above Oxbow Village, Oxbow Dam and Brownlee Dam, located upstream on Snake River.

The Iron Dyke copper deposit discovery site is on the south wall of Iron Dyke Creek about 2,500 feet west and 300 feet above Snake River at Homestead. Frank E. Pearce, while employed at the mine located a homestead claim covering part of the alluvial fan below the mine prompting residents to adopt the name Homestead for the settlement that grew along the river near the mine. J. H. Pearson erected a large tent, turned it into a general store, and became the first postmaster. Later the mining company built and maintained housing and schools for employees and families. Approximately 150 men lived at Homestead during the height of mine production. The town had two stores, a post office, meat market, and gas station.

Master mechanic Rudy Lanning and his wife, Mona, came to work for the company in 1915. They remained there as caretakers long after closure of the mine in 1928. Mona still lived at Homestead in 1979 (Conley, *et al.,* p.133)

The Iron Dyke Mine ore bodies are massive sulfide deposits in volcanic rocks in the upper part of the Hunsaker Creek Formation of Permian age (Bussey and LeAnderson, 1994, and Vallier, 1998, p. 115) The deposits were formed around hot springs on and beneath an Early Permian sea floor. The system was driven by cooling magma beneath the sea floor. Sulfide minerals in order of abundance were pyrite, chalcopyrite, sphalerite and galena.

A large amount of exploration and development work had been done and a 50-tons-per-day mill was built to process Iron Dyke ore bodies by the time the O.R. & N. railroad from Huntington reached Homestead in 1909, but there was little production before 1915 when the demands of World War I caused copper prices to increase. The initial product of the mine was pyrite mined from upper parts of the deposit and used for flux at smelters treating copper ores from mines in the Seven Devils mining district in Idaho on the opposite side of Snake River.

Halstead Lindsley (Parks and Swartley, 1916, p.132) or Halsted Lindsay (Conley, etal, p. 133) of New York or Colorado became general manager of the mine in 1915. Shipment of gold and silver-bearing copper ore to custom smelters began in August. During the first year of operation, 462 fifty-ton railcar loads of crude ore were shipped, which averaged 6 percent copper and about $5 per ton of gold and silver. A 150-ton flotation mill was placed in operation in September 1916 and from then on most of the ore that was too low-grade to ship crude was concentrated before being shipped to a smelter. The mill crushed the ore, concentrated the valuable minerals, and discarded the waste rock so that the amount of material that needed to be shipped to smelters was greatly reduced. Operations ceased in 1928. Production during the years 1915-1928 amounted to 35,967 ounces of gold, 256,489 ounces of silver, and 14,417,920 pounds of copper from 209,589 tons of ore milled and 29,486 tons of ore smelted. Ore and concentrates were shipped to the International Smelter at Salt Lake City, Utah.

During the 1915-1928 stage of production, ore was developed and mined via a glory hole, 4 adit levels, a 650-foot vertical shaft and 500-foot inclined shaft driven into the south wall of Iron Dyke Creek near the discovery site. An adit near the mouth of Iron Dyke Creek and only a few 10's of feet above the high-water level of Snake River was driven into the ore zone in 1942-43 during an exploration program, including a large amount of diamond-drilling, conducted by the Butler Ore Company of Saint Paul, Minnesota, owners of the property at that time.

Copperfield, Homestead District.

In 1974 Texas Gulf, Inc., a large mining company, leased the mine from the Butler Ore Company, rehabilitated the river-level adit and in succeeding years conducted extensive diamond drilling. The diamond drilling program was designed to determine the amount and grade of ore remaining in the old mine. In 1979, based on results of the drilling, Texas Gulf bought the mine and other property from the Butler company for about $1.500,000 and formed a joint venture agreement with Silver King Mines, Inc.

Company reports indicate that the mine was operated fairly consistently in 1979-1981 and sporadically in 1984 and 1986-1987. During the 1979-1987 period, the mine reportedly produced 68,000 tons of ore yielding 20,400 ounces of gold, 3,580,000 pounds of copper, and 34,000 ounces of silver. The 1986-87 operations completed mining of all of the developed ore and the mine has been closed since late November 1987. Total production 1915-1928 and 1979-1987 was 23,267,920 pounds of copper, 58,017 ounces of gold, and 219,989 ounces of silver.

Kleinschmidt Grade starts on the Idaho bank of Snake River five miles north of Oxbow, climbs 2,350 feet in 5.5 miles into the Seven Devils region of Idaho, and along the way provides spectacular views of the upper reaches of Hells Canyon and the eastern part of Oregon's Wallowa Mountains. At Cuprum (about 4,300 feet elevation) a small ghost town 9.5 miles from Snake River, the road passes between rows of well-maintained cabins and a small store. Branches from this road east of Cuprum reach elevations of more than 7,000 feet; four wheel drive vehicles required.

The grade was built in 1889-1891 by Albert Kleinschmidt to serve his and other copper mines in the Seven Devils mining district including the now long abandoned mining camps of Landore and

Above: Iron Dyke mill, at Homestead. The Iron Dyke mine produced copper and gold and silver during two periods of operation, 1915-1928 and 1979-1987. Below: Iron Dyke Mine, air view, ca. 1980s. The small light colored spots near the bottom of the draw (Iron Dyke Creek) are waste dumps made adjacent to mine entryways during the 1915 to 1928 stage of mining. In 1943 a new adit started near the mouth of the draw and 300 feet lower gave access to the ore zone during the 1970s to 1980s stage of activity. Below: The dashed line marks the contact between layered young (Tertiary) basaltic lava flows above and folded old (Permian and Triassic) oceanic rocks.

Helena. Hauling the ore more than one hundred miles by wagons to Weiser, Idaho, and by rail from there to smelters was so costly that only high grade ore could be mined and high grade ore was running out. Kleinschmidt's plan was to haul the ore down to Snake River, transfer it to a steamboat, and haul it up river to the railroad near Huntington. Unfortunately, the steamboat he had built, named Norma, proved incapable of negotiating the rapids in the river under heavy load. The grade was never used to haul ore down to the river, but 90 years later the Iron Dyke Mine at Homestead began hauling ore up the grade to a mill at the Copper Cliff Mine 2.5 miles beyond Cuprum.

The grade was built using dynamite, horse drawn scrapers, and hand labor. It is well graded and usually well maintained but it is crooked and narrow, mostly a one-track road with turnouts. (Local inquiry about the condition of the road is advisable before use.) In 1893, Eli Ballard established a ferry connecting Kleinschmidt's road with a road on the Oregon side of the Snake River. The Oregon landing was at the mouth of Ballard Creek. A bridge was built across the river at Ballard's Ferry in 1926. It was removed in 1966 when the bridge at Oxbow was built

Homestead was the northern terminus of the Snake River branch of the Oregon and Washington Railroad and Navigation Company's line 58 miles north of Huntington. Five miles below Homestead the boundary between Baker and Wallowa counties crosses the Snake River. A paved road extends from Oxbow along the Idaho side of the river to Hells Canyon Dam, then crosses the dam and continues along the Oregon shore for about a mile and ends at a U. S. Forest Service visitor center. A trail continues along the river about a mile and from there the canyon is impassable except by boat. For 125 miles northward as far as Asotin, Washington, a few miles above Lewiston, Idaho, Snake River flows through one of the most remarkable canyons in the United States. Measured on the Idaho side of the river it is deeper than the Grande Canyon of the Colorado River. In order to preserve the natural beauty of the canyon, Congress created Hells Canyon National Recreation Area (652,488 acres) in December 1975. Congress also established Hells Canyon Wilderness Area (190,000 acres) and the 32-miles-long Snake River Wild and Scenic River corridor extending from Hells Canyon Dam to Pittsburgh Landing.

> **Kleinschmidt's plan was to haul the ore down to Snake River, transfer it to a steamboat and haul it up river to the railroad near Huntington. Unfortunately, the steamboat he had built, named Norma, proved incapable of negotiating the rapids in the river under heavy load.**

The book *Islands and Rapids, A Geologic Story Of Hells Canyon* by Tracy Vallier, is a highly informative treatise on the geology and people of Hells Canyon. Vallier has spent much of his career mapping the geology of the canyon.

Two different views of Homestead., on Snake River.
Home of Iron Dyke Mine.

Homestead general store.

Homestead., Oregon, on the Snake River.
Note on right of photo the railroad from Huntington.

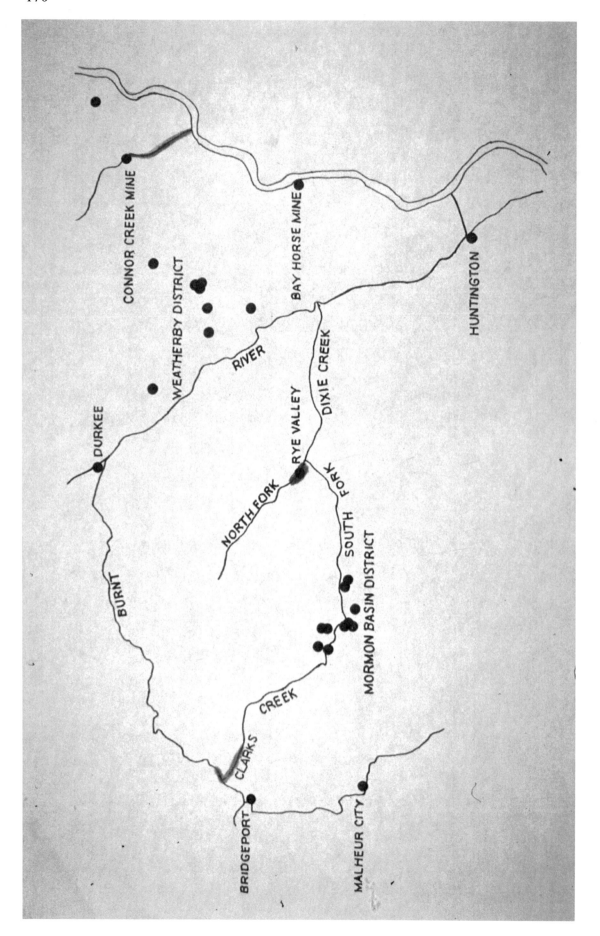

Map of Southeastern Blue Mountains

Southeastern Blue Mountains

This region includes the lower parts of the Burnt River and Willow Creek drainages, from their mouths on Snake River, to their origins in south-central Baker County and north-central Malheur County.

The clusters of gold-quartz veins and gold placer deposits in the region including the Mormon Basin, Weatherby, and Connor Creek districts are associated with small northeasterly aligned exposures of granodiorite including the Lookout Mountain, Pedro Mountain, and Cow Valley Butte stocks. Older host rocks are metamorphosed rocks of the Burnt River schist, and gabbro, diorite, and serpentinized intrusive rocks.

Between Clarks Creek at the lower end of Bridgeport Valley to the upper end of Durkee Valley, Burnt River has cut a narrow canyon through old metamorphic rocks, including schistose sedimentary and volcanic rocks, limestone, diorite, and gabbro. The limestone probably was deposited as layers between layers of sedimentary and volcanic rocks, but due to subsequent intense folding and faulting, the rocks of the region are visible now as widely scattered large and small blocks. The many twists and turns of the river road yield spectacular views of the deformed rocks on both sides of the canyon.

Lookout Mountain at 7,120 feet is the topographic high point in the region and is one of northeast Oregon's most visible land marks. The topographic low at the mouth of Burnt River is at 2,077 feet, the highwater mark of Brownlee Reservoir. Below Durkee Valley, Burnt River flows in a canyon of more subdued topograpy between Lookout Mountain and Pedro Mountain until it reaches Snake River about a mile below Huntington.

The largest lode gold producers have been the Connor Creek Mine in the Connor Creek District, the Gold Ridge Mine in the Weatherby District, and the Rainbow, Humboldt, and Sunday Hill mines in the Mormon Basin District. Lindgren stated (1901), "The belt extending from Connor Creek by Weatherby, Chicken Creek, Rye Valley, Humboldt, Clarks Creek and Malheur was formerly the most important gold mining region in the State and still maintains a diminishing production."

Placer gold production from deposits in the southeastern Blue Mountains began in 1862. Early-day output, particularly from the drainage area of the Mormon Basin District, reputedly was quite large although official records are scarce. Most of the gravel covering the floor of Mormon Basin and the 5-miles-long-channel of Basin Creek below Mormon Basin has been worked at one time or another. The Pleistocene bench placers at Rye Valley produced more than $1,000,000 in gold by 1914 (Swartley, 1914). Gravel deposits in the floodplains of lower Clarks Creek and adjacent Burnt River were worked first by hydraulic methods and later (1917-1936) by floating dredge. The famed early-day gulch placers of Malheur, Eldorado, and Amelia were worked in part by water provided by the 125-miles-long Eldorado Ditch that was completed in 1873.

Placer mining has continued in parts of most of these areas; however, for many decades, mining operations have been small and sporadic. Because of the scarcity of water for mining, some of the placers, particularly those of elevated floodplains, have not been thoroughly exploited.

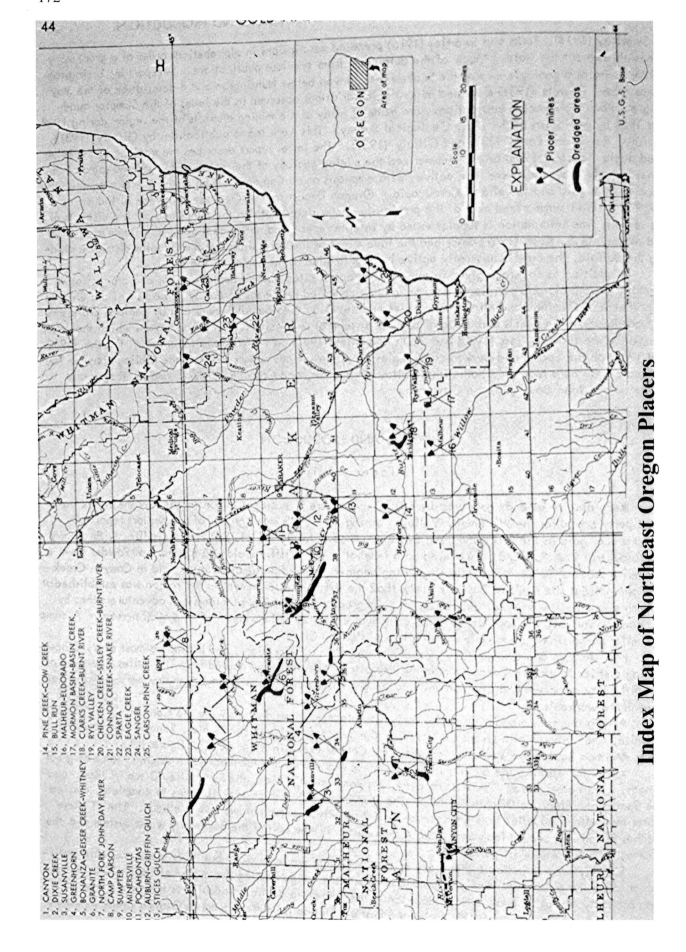

1. CANYON
2. DIXIE CREEK
3. SUSANVILLE
4. GREENHORN
5. BONANZA-GEISER CREEK-WHITNEY
6. GRANITE
7. NORTH FORK JOHN DAY RIVER
8. CAMP CARSON
9. SUMPTER
10. MINERSVILLE
11. POCAHONTAS
12. AUBURN-GRIFFIN GULCH
13. STICES GULCH

14. PINE CREEK-COW CREEK
15. BULL RUN
16. MALHEUR-ELDORADO
17. MORMON BASIN-BASIN CREEK.
18. CLARKS CREEK-BURNT RIVER
19. RYE VALLEY
20. CHICKEN CREEK-SISLEY CREEK-BURNT RIVER.
21. CONNOR CREEK-SNAKE RIVER
22. SPARTA
23. EAGLE CREEK
24. SANGER
25. CARSON-PINE CREEK

Index Map of Northeast Oregon Placers

Connor Creek Mine three miles upstream
from creek's confluence with Snake River.

Connor Creek District

Connor Creek District encompases the western side of Snake River Canyon between the mouths of Burnt River on the south and Powder River on the north. Connor Creek flows into the Snake River about 14 miles below Powder River in about the middle of the district.

Rocks exposed in the district include greenstone, slate, phyllite, low grade schist, and old plutonic rocks of Permian and Late Triassic age. These rocks have been intruded by Jurassic-Cretaceous granodiorite. Lookout Mountain is the largest exposure of the granodiorite.

Lode deposits in the Connor Creek District include quartz veins and irregular quartz-impregnated fracture zones in slate, phyllite, and metavolcanic rocks. A minimum of $1,250,000 (67,000 ounces) gold about 900 fine has been produced, almost entirely from the Connor Creek Mine. The Bay Horse Mine produced about 286,000 ounces of silver.

The Connor Creek Mine is at the fork of Connor Creek and its tributary, Dry Creek, about three miles up Connor Creek from Snake River and about 18 miles downriver from Huntington. Albert Burch said the deposit was discovered by Wood and Eidelman in 1871. It was among the first lode mines operated in northeastern Oregon.

Work was started in 1871, but there is no record of production until a mill was built in the late 1870s. The main period of activity was in 1880-1890 when $1,250,000 in gold and silver was extracted from the mine. There are no records of production since that time. Burch says that during much of the 1880-1890 period the mine was owned by Simeon Reed, whose widow in later years was a founder of Reed College in Portland, Oregon. Using money from the Connor Creek Mine, Reed purchased interest in the Bunker Hill and Sullivan Mine in Idaho. Cash from the sale of the latter mine started Reed College on its exemplary career.

Densley (1987) tells us that a small town grew adjacent to the lower portal of the mine. About $20,000 was produced in 1915-1918 by a company formed by J. H. Badgley, Albert Geiser, and Isaac Sweet.

Densley states that Reed sent Captain Josiah Myrick to manage the mine and camp. Myrick stayed there as caretaker until his death long after the mine ceased active operations. Densley also says Myrick was a seafaring man and river navigator. He was captain for many years of steamboats on the Willamette, Columbia, and Snake Rivers. He piloted the first steamboat, the Shoshone, on the Snake River above Huntington for Oregon Steam Navigation Company on May 16, 1865. Reed first sent Myrick to Sparta to manage the Gem Mine. It was not operating so Myrick was sent on to Connor Creek. Burch (1941, p. 112) says Reed hired as manager of the Connor Creek mine a brilliant young engineer named Victor M. Clement. When Reed acquired the Bunker Hill and Sullivan Mine, he transferred Clement to that scene of action.

Swartley (1914, p. 216) says Connor Creek gold was in a quartz vein of 3 to 4 feet average thickness in slatey argillite and greenstone. The gold was about 900 fine. The vein strikes north 40^0

west and dips 70^0 to 75^0 southwest. Mill ore ran from \$3 to \$10 per ton, but several rich pockets were found in which coarse gold was associated with argentite in white quartz. A *Baker Herald* news article (July 13, 1901) reports that Captain Myrick had assembled a "celebrated collection of nuggets" from the Connor Creek mine including a peck of small slabs and wire-like gold in white quartz. The newspaper also reported that "from 140 pounds of rock \$2,000 worth of gold (96.7 troy ounces) was taken, not counting the specimens." So much mercury was contained in the ore that amalgamators had difficulty maintaining a proper hardness of the amalgamation plates. Swartley continues, "The vein has been developed by 6 tunnels over a vertical interval of 1000 feet, the shortest 500 feet and the longest 3,700 feet, at present mostly caved. Total length of underground workings exceeds 8000 feet. Stopes on all levels continue in northwesterly direction until a fault is reached. The fault strikes E and dips 45^0 to 65^0 southeast. The vein has been picked up on the other side of the fault only on the lowest level and has not been developed." The mine had closed 20 years before Swartley's visit.

Connor Creek Placer

Mining of placer deposits along Connor Creek below the Connor Creek mine led to the discovery of the Connor Creek vein. Lindgren (1901) said that the placers were worked twice before 1900. Total output to 1914 was about \$125,000 (Swartley, 1914). Small periodic output has continued to the present time. Since 1914 various parts of the creek have been worked periodically by small operators.

Bay Horse Mine

The Bay Horse Mine is on a steep slope a few hundred feet above Snake River seven miles below Huntington. The mine produced 145,459.54 troy ounces of silver from 4,895 tons of ore shipped to smelters during 1920-1925 and was operated for short periods in the 1980's. Total production was about 286,000 ounces of silver. The Bay Horse deposits are small and of irregular shape in a poorly defined west-trending fracture zone cutting andesite and rhyolitic rocks of Late Triassic age. The fault zone is weakly silicified locally. Silver-bearing tennantite, the only silver-bearing ore mineral recognized, forms thin seams and small clots in the silicified rock. The ore contains practically no gold.

Ibex Minerals, Inc., began a rehabilitation and exploration program in 1975. Ibex was joined by Centennial Exploration Co. to continue exploration. By 1976, the mine's main haulage level had been rehabilitated for about 1,000 feet and raises had been driven to gain access to the intermediate level. Two drill stations were cut in the lower level for exploratory diamond drilling to test the extent of the mineralized horizon visible in the intermediate level.

Silver King Mines, Inc., became operator of the mine in 1984 under a lease agreement between Silver King and Western Lands and Resources. Silver King produced about 6,000 tons of ore averaging 12 ounces of silver per ton in 1984 The ore was treated at Silver King's flotation mill near Cuprum, Idaho. About 1,000 feet of underground work and 15,000 feet of drilling were done in 1984. The Bay Horse mine is developed by about 1,800 feet of drifts and crosscuts in Upper Triassic metavolcanic rocks near their contact with unconformably overlying Jurassic graywacke.

*Placer mines on
Basin Creek below
Mormon Basin.*

Quartz Gulch Placer

*Quartz Gulch
Placer 2*

Snake River Placers

Brownlee Reservoir inundated thousands of acres of farms and ranch land and many small placer mines. Parts of several gulches, alluvial fans, and gravel terraces above water level of the reservoir show evidence of having been mined for placer gold. Before 1900, a consortium of Frenchmen dug a ditch extending from Daley Creek west of the canyon rim to placer deposits on the Snake River slope near the mouth of Alder Creek. Walt Forsea (2006), long-time local cattle rancher, says that very little ground in the Alder Creek area has been disturbed by mining and there is no record of gold production from that source. Densley (1987) says that during the depression of the 1930s and early 1940s, several families and individuals supplemented their meager incomes by placer mining along Snake River. Some worked part time on farms and ranches for land owners along the river. Some lived in dugouts.

Some Snake River miners found gold below water level and many believed that the closer one got to the middle of the river the more gold there would be. Various methods of working in water too deep to wade were devised but none was very successful. Forsea recalls working from a small boat anchored to the river bottom and using an ordinary hand shovel to scoop gravel off the bottom and put it in tubs and buckets aboard the boat. Gold, if any was found, was separated from the gravel by panning. Working belly deep in water was difficult, but one compensating factor was that on hot summer days when daytime temperatures were in the 100-plus range the water had a cooling effect that made the work tolerable, especially when one was finding gold.

Swede Olson Placer

Franz (Swede) Olson was born in Nebraska. As a young man he came west to the Fruitland-Payette, Idaho, area to buy apples and had them shipped by rail to sell in Nebraska markets. He later spent time mining and fur trapping in the Salmon River country in Idaho. He then moved to the Fruitland area of Idaho, then to Snake River in 1931, where he acquired some placer mining claims near Quicksilver Creek on which he established his future home: a railroad boxcar that had been used by the Oregon Short Line Railroad on its run down Snake River from Huntington to Robinette and Homestead. Shortly before the innundation of his 1931 homesite by the filling of Brownlee Reservoir in 1958, Idaho Power Company paid to have his boxcar home moved to the present site of Swede's Landing above the new high water level. Swede's cabin was adjacent to a busy road. He was friendly man and many visitors to the area stopped to visit with him. He would talk about most anything pertaining to the river except how much gold he had taken from it.

Swede lost one eye by mishandling dynamite and carried shotgun pellets just beneath the skin of his back put there by an irate neighbor who mistakenly thought Swede was encroaching on his claim and stealing his gold. Swede saw the man coming toward him carrying a shotgun and swearing to kill him. Swede ran but was hit by several pellets from a shotgun blast. After the man cooled down and other neighbors, and possibly a sheriff's deputy, had convinced him that he was out of control mentally and needed help, Swede hauled his assailant to town to the hospital.

Humboldt Mine, Mormon Basin District.

Huntington, 1915.

Walt Forsea (2006), who was administrator of Swede's estate, told me on January 19, 2006, that he saw Swede's gold accumulation in a lock box in a Weiser, Idaho, bank and guessed there was about $150,000 (at $600 per ounce) worth of gold there. There were several nuggets, the largest being the size of a walnut. After Swede's death and at his request, the gold was given to his cousins living in Nebraska.

Forsea said Swede worked the placer mostly in winter months when the Forseas allowed him use of water from a ditch they owned. In summer time Swede worked for wages on farms and orchards near Fruitland. Forsea also said that to his knowledge Swede did not sell any of the gold he mined but, before his death, gave some of it away to special friends and in-laws.

The Forsea Family and Their Ranch

Patriarch Dan Forsea came alone from the old country, Romania, at the age of 16. Dan and wife, Blanche, both worked for the Baker Ranch on Snake River helping to harvest fruit. They met there and married. Dan bought a section (640 acres) of homestead land in the vicinity of Big Deacon Creek in 1918 for about $1.50 per acre. They and their decendents continued buying land and their holdings in the canyon area eventually totaled about 5,000 acres. Their home was on Big Deacon Creek. They had 5 children: Harold, Bob, Margaret, Walter, and Pearl. Bob and Margaret have passed on. Harold taught school most of his career. He died at 92. Members of the the Forsea family have maintained and added to their property in the canyon, but all had moved out of the canyon before their land along the river was inundated by the waters of Brownlee Reservoir in 1958.

Weatherby (also called Lower Burnt River District)

This district includes the drainage of Burnt River from Cave Creek and Deer Creek south to Snake River.

DOGAMI Bulletin 14-A (1939) briefly describes 14 small gold mines and prospects, both lode and placer. Among the lode mines, the largest producer was Gold Ridge. Others include Gold Hill, Little Bonanza, Little Hill, Gleason, and Hallock. In this area also are small placers on Burnt River, Chicken Creek, and various tributaries. Lode deposits occur in small, discontinuous quartz veins, mainly in granodiorite.

Lode production probably totaled 5,000-10,000 ounces. Gold Ridge and other small mines produced about $210,000 between 1881 and 1886 with a 10-stamp mill says Lindgren (1901). Oxidized ore ran $12 to $15 per ton in gold about 870 fine. Gold Ridge mine developed three veins in granodiorite and older metamorphic rocks. The ore zones are intruded by small offshoots of the granodioritic Pedro Mountain stock that borders the district on the northeast. Gold mineralization probably was related to emplacement of the stock and related bodies.

Mormon Basin District

Mormon Basin District is centered about 25 miles south of Baker City, Oregon, in the southeastern part of the Blue Mountains. The basin is a small south-sloping, sediment-filled depression near the top of the high divide between Willow Creek, a tributary of the Malheur River to the south and Burnt River to the north and east. Gravel and dirt roads enter the basin from the north, east, and south. The district was noted by early writers for the richness of its placer gold deposits but there are few records of placer production. Lode mines later produced more than 180,500 ounces of gold and a nearly equal amount of silver, most of it prior to 1920. There has been very little mine production for many decades. Rocks exposed in the district are chiefly metamorphosed sedimentary, volcanic, and mafic intrusive rocks of pre-Jurassic age and granodioritic instrusive rocks of Late Jurassic-Early Cretaceous age. Mafic and silicic volcanic rocks and tuffaceous sedimentary rocks of Tertiary age cover the old rocks locally. Elevations range from about 3,550 feet on Basin Creek at the south edge of the district to 6,455 feet at the top of Pedro Mountain in the northeastern part. The land supports mainly rangeland grasses and brush and scattered patches of pine and fir trees. Industries in the region are chiefly cattle ranching and occasional timber production and placer gold mining.

Rich gold placer deposits were discovered in Mormon Basin (also known as Humboldt Basin in the early days) in 1862 and for two or three decades thereafter the district was well known as an important placer mining camp (Raymond, 1870; Lindgren, 1901). Raymond said that a nugget weighing 40 ounces worth $640 was found in 1866 and that men using crudely built rockers "realized as much as $70 to $90 per day of eight hours. Mining is carried on with iron and canvas hydraulic pipes, or with ground sluices. A pocket vein, the Niagra Vein in Humboldt Basin, furnished in 1863 some remarkable specimens of quartz studded with gold." Although none of the early writers offered an estimate of production, Swartley (1914) said, "The amount is quite large." The placer camps in Mormon Basin and at Amelia likely produced most of the gold credited to Malheur County (Lindgren, 1901). Partial records credit placer mines in Mormon Basin with slightly over 3,000 ounces of gold valued at $75,200 during operations in 1882 and 1883 (Lindgren, 1901).

Gold-bearing gravels covered parts of the floor and west margin of Mormon Basin and extended along the 5-mile long channel of Basin Creek south of Mormon Basin. Hand and hydraulic placer mining in the 1860s -1890s left extensive hillside cuts and hand stacked boulder piles along the western margin of Mormon Basin and the west-facing slope of lower Basin Creek. Mechanized equipment, including draglines and washing plants were used in later years to work gravel deposits in the central part of Mormon Basin, gravel deposits in parts of the flood plain of Basin Creek, and coarse bench gravels on the east side of Basin Creek. The placer pit in the central part of Mormon Basin is a mile long and from 700 to 1,000 feet wide. Much of the pit is floored by a layer, thickness unknown, of moderately indurated lake sediments composed mostly of clay, silt, and sand with some gravel locally. Miners called the material "webfoot" or "false bedrock." Similar, though less indurated deposits, are exposed along the pit's margins. Evidently the latter, mostly fine-grained, deposits were not economically mineable. Thickness of the gold-bearing gravel and sand overlying the false bedrock is said to have averaged about 16 feet (Wagner, 1967). The Mormon Basin Placers were last operated in mid-1980s. Veta Grande reported production of 1,654 ounces of gold in 1980 and 1,973 ounces of gold in 1981. The 1982 production is unknown, but probably small.

Scarcity of water and the shallow gradient of the basin floor made mining difficult. Basin Creek carries little water except during spring runoff. Some of the water used for placer mining operations was pumped from the shaft of the Humboldt Mine.

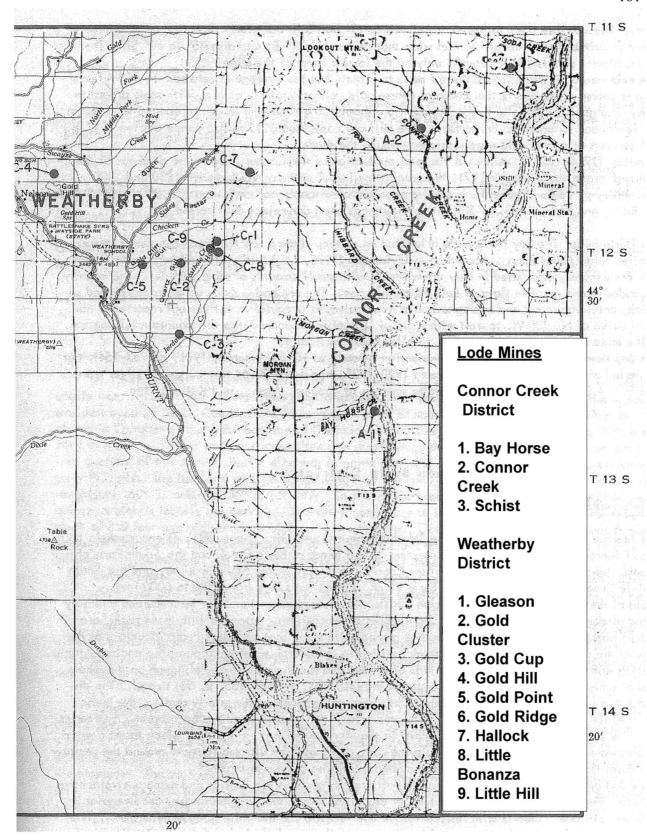

Lode Mines

Connor Creek District

1. Bay Horse
2. Connor Creek
3. Schist

Weatherby District

1. Gleason
2. Gold Cluster
3. Gold Cup
4. Gold Hill
5. Gold Point
6. Gold Ridge
7. Hallock
8. Little Bonanza
9. Little Hill

Index Map of Connor Creek, and Weatherby Districts

Rainbow Mine

The Rainbow Mine is a short distance east of Mormon Basin at the head of Rainbow Gulch that drains northeastward into Dixie Creek. Elmer and Hogg say that the Rainbow Mine worked two near-parallel quartz veins, one on each wall of a northeast trending shear zone that varied from a few feet to 50 feet wide in phylite and altered volcanic rock. The shear zone includes a felsic dike that was intensely altered during mineralization. The most productive vein is on the footwall of the shear zone and strikes N 60^0 E and dips 55^0 to 65^0 NW (Swartley, 1914). The ore zone had strike length of 1,500 feet and dip depth of 500 feet. The ore shoots were as much as 350 feet long. The gold was largely free milling. Sulfides included small quantities of pyrite, arsenopyrite, galena, sphalerite, tetrahedrite, along with quartz, ankerite, fuchsite, and gold. Some of the best ore was in breccia zones between the altered hornblende porphyry dike and country rock.

Recorded production from the mine is $2,323,092 during 1901-1919 and 1,222 troy ounces in 1934. Average grade of ore treated was 0.48 ounce per ton.

Humboldt Mine

The Humboldt Vein is in schist and amphibolite, strikes east, and dips 75^0 north (Gilluly or Lindgren). The main vein is in quartz-mica schist, strikes N 45^0 W, and dips 50^0 N. Average mining width was 2 1\2 feet. Gangue includes quartz and fault gouge, pyrite, and lesser arsenopyrite, galena, and sphalerite.

Rocks on the surface of the Humboldt waste dump are about 50 percent amphibolite, some apparently derived from altered porphyritic and vesicular metavolcanic rocks and some from coarse gabbro, 35 percent meta-argillite and meta-chert and about 15 percent talc schist. The slope west of the shaft is mostly amphibolite, with some meta-argillite.

Sunday Hill

For many years the Sunday Hill Mine buildings were used as living quarters for a field camp for geology students from the University of Oregon. The mine was first operated in 1868. Total production has been about $100,000. The mine was acquired by Capri Resources, Ltd. of Vancouver, B.C., in 1983. Seven diamond drill holes were drilled in 1984. Results were disappointing.

Sunday Hill Mine. Photo courtesy of Doris King.

Country rocks are foliated sedimentary rocks of the Burnt River Schist with quartz diorite intruding the schist. The workings expose several veins consisting chiefly of quartz and fault gouge.

Left: Panama Placer. Mining gravel underground and washing it through a sluice box to extract the gold.

Below: Rainbow Mine, Mormon Basin District, produced $2.3 million in gold during 1900-1919.

Basin Creek Placers

Gravel deposits along Basin Creek below Mormon Basin and terrace gravels on the east bench overlooking the creek have been worked periodically since gold was discovered in the Malheur City-Mormon Basin area in the early 1860s. Most of the old placers are in Sec. 32, T. 13 S., R. 42 E. and Secs. 5 and 8, T. 14 S., R. 42 E. The terrace deposits are about 150 feet above the level of Basin Creek.

Among the latest operators was Basin Creek Mines, Inc., who began placer mining on Basin Creek in 1974. Later they worked terrace gravels east of Basin Creek. Water was pumped from the creek and recirculated through settling ponds constructed adjacent to the creek. The washing plant handled about 60 yards per hour. Water is scarce except in early spring. Development includes an open cut about 1,500 feet long and 100 to 500 feet wide. The June through September, 1976, production was about 1,000 ounces of gold. A group named Delta Investors took over the mine and continued the operation during the late 1970s and early 1980s.

Most of the gravel is under a foot in diameter. Some boulders exceed two feet. Bedrock is sandstone and siltstone of the Weatherby Formation.

Clarksville Placers

Clarks Creek heads on the north side of the ridge opposite the head of Basin Creek and runs nearly due north into Burnt River at the lower end of Bridgeport Valley. Gold was discovered on Clarks Creek in the summer of 1862 by a group of prospectors from Auburn looking for new diggings. The creek was named for a member of the group named Clark who accidentally shot himself. While waiting for Clark to recover from his wound, his companions found gold mixed in the gravel of the creek bed and started mining. The mining camp was called Clarksville. The townsite, long ago abandoned, is about three miles up Clarks Creek from Burnt River and three miles straight east of Bridgeport.

J. W. Virtue, born in Ireland and raised in Canada, arrived in Clarksville in summer 1863 at age 26 and there spent the first two or three years of his long career as a mining man. Virtue kept a diary of his experiences during the year 1864. Most of that diary is quoted in an article by Gary Dielman published in the Spring 2004 issue of *Oregon Historical Quarterly*. Virtue later became sheriff of Baker County (1866-1870) and established the first bank in Baker City (1870). He was once part owner of the Virtue Mine.

An unpublished book by students of Burnt River High School says that in its heyday Clarksville had two general stores; one, owned by Jere Dooley, housed the Post Office. The town also included two hotels, a boarding house run by Mrs. Daniel Elliott, a saloon, and a brewery. The school was housed in private homes. One of the first teachers was Helen Stack who began her long career as an educator at Clarksville school at the age of 16. Later the Helen M. Stack Junior High School in Baker City was named in her honor. Dooley and Elliott descendants remain in the region. Clarksville's population in 1870 was 224 (141 Chinese, 83 whites). The Chinese were the last to leave as the gold ran out. One small stone building remains to mark the site of Clarksville.

Stereopticon view of placer excavation in Rye Valley.

Rye Valley 1900. Placer excavations on the slope to the right of the creek (North Fork of Dixie Creek) yielded about $1,000,000 in gold prior to Swartley's visit in 1914.

B. F. Koontz recognized the need for lumber and built a sawmill near the mouth of Mill Creek which enters Burnt River a few miles above the mouth of Clarks Creek. Water to operate the mill was brought from Burnt River by ditch.

Gravel in the lower part of Clarks Creek and in Burnt River just below Clarks Creek was worked sporadically by small flume dredge during 1917-1936. There was little or no production during several of those years. Total output recorded by the U.S. Bureau of Mines was 22,572 ounces of gold and 2,706 ounces of silver. Operators at different times were Oregon Dredge Company and Superior Dredge Company. Part-time miners have continued to work or rework gravel deposits along various parts of Clarks Creek to the present time.

A puzzling chapter of the geologic history of the area is that the rounded rock fragments making up the gravel deposits in the bed of Clarks Creek are much coarser and more abundant in the lower part of the creek than in the upper part and peculiar rock types, including jade (nephrite) and related tremolite-actinolite-rich rocks, found as boulders in the lower part of the creek have not been found anywhere in the present drainage area feeding into the creek.

Rye Valley Placers

Rye Valley is a small valley located just above the junction between the north and south forks of Dixie Creek about five miles west by graveled road from U.S. Highway I-84 and the junction of Dixie Creek with Burnt River.

The hydraulic mining of Pleistocene bench placers along the west side of the North Fork of Dixie Creek in Rye Valley produced more than $1,000,000 in gold by 1914 (Swartley, 1914). Mining began in 1862. Raymond (1870) said Rye Valley placers had been worked successfully for the four years prior to his visit in 1869. Gold was about 740 fine.

Malheur City District, including Eldorado and Amelia

These placer gold mining camps, located in the sagebrush and desert grasses covered mountainous country of northern Malheur County, were among the most famous early day placer camps in the Blue Mountains. They are on the Willow Creek (south) side of the Burnt River--Willow Creek divide about 35 miles south of Baker City, accessed by good country roads from the north via Bridgeport and from the east via Huntington.

The Eldorado Ditch, built between 1862 and 1873, mostly by Chinese labor, carried water to these diggings from as far away as the South Fork of Burnt River, more than 100 miles. Placer mining has continued in parts of these areas, although for many decades mining operations generally have been small and sporadic. Because of the scarcity of water for mining, some of the placers, particularly those on elevated floodplains, have not been thoroughly exploited.

Lindgren (1901, p. 773) said the gulches were filled with 6 to 30 feet of gravels of fine texture which, at the time of his visit, were almost exhausted. Shasta Gulch is the main watercourse. It and Rich Gulch were the most productive.

Express Ranch (present day Durkee)was a popular resting place for prospectors and travelers of all kinds. Express Ranch was established ca. 1863, shortly after the discovery of gold at Auburn. The owner, C. W. Durkee, gave his name to the present town.

Clarksville was named for a man who accidentally shot himself. While he was healing enough to travel his companions found gold in the creek gravel. This led to a small rush of miners to the creek and establishment of a small town called Clarksville.

In 1870, following his visit in 1869, Raymond said Eldorado City and Malheur City were flourishing towns in Baker County. Other principal towns in Baker County were Auburn, Baker City, Express Ranch, and Amelia. Malheur City, Eldorado City, and Amelia became the first towns in Malheur County when Malheur County was carved from Baker County on February 17, 1887. Rich Gulch and Shasta Gulch were the most productive of several gulches in the district. Fifty-two miles of the Eldorado Ditch had been completed (8 ½ feet wide at the top, six feet at bottom, and three feet deep, with a capacity of 3,000 miners inches of water). Carter and Packwood had 200 Chinese building the ditch. The company, named Malheur and Burnt River Consolidated Ditch and Mining Co., had as its officers president B. D. Buford, Rock Island, Illinois, and superintendent, J. H. Johnson, Eldorado, Oregon. The company ran two stores receiving goods directly from Chicago.

From *Argus Observer* (Ontario, Oregon), comes the following information about the construction of the Eldorado Ditch: Most of the ditch builders were Chinese. They were paid about a dollar per ten-hour day and boarded themselves. The whites' wages were a little higher. The Chinese worked all summer in the placer mines, then spent the winter months in Malheur City. Common winter pastimes were playing a gambling game called "Fan-Tan" and smoking opium.

Eldorado City and Malheur City

No physical evidence remains to show where the mining town of Eldorado was located. Ray Duncan and Carroll Locey said Eldorado was about three miles north and west of Malheur City. The Bridgeport quadrangle topographic map shows Eldorado (site) about 1.5 miles northwest of the Malheur City Cemetery and a few old foundations mark the former site of that town. Malheur City became a ghost town and then was destroyed by a range fire in 1957.

In an article in the *Argus Observer* of September 21, 1944, J. R. Greg says prospectors from Auburn discovered valuable gold deposits in present Mormon Basin and in 1865 other rich discoveries were made on upper Willow Creek. The latter area became known as the Shasta Mining District. Shasta Gulch, Rich Gulch, and Quartz Gulch were the most productive of several gulches that were mined in the area. The town of Eldorado was started to serve the miners in 1868 when "Charles Goodnough, Stephenson Bros. and a Mr. Kirkpatrick erected store buildings and each firm engaged in the mercantile business. S. B. Reed erected a hotel and for the next two years, Eldorado was a thriving mining camp. In 1870, Wm S. Glenn, Lake Bros and George Collins, with his sister Mary Collins erected three new store buildings on land owned by William Morfitt a mile or two south of Eldorado and the town of Malheur City came into existence nearer the banks of the Eldorado ditch and the office of the ditch company was also established here." Most of the two-year-old buildings in Eldorado were moved to the new town.

Duncan (September 4, 1969) gives a different perspective on when mining began in the Shasta-Eldorado area when he said, "Bill Boswell told me that his folks moved to Eldorado in 1864 and the place was a boom town when they arrived there. Bill says there were more than a thousand people in Eldorado at that time and they were digging gold…. The Eldorado or 'Big Ditch' was surveyed and started in 1863. It was originally intended to furnish water to the Clarks Creek 'Diggings' but was later changed and taken to Shasta District instead. The work seemed to have stood still from 1863 to 1867 when 11 miles were dug. It was completed to Malheur City in 1870." Woodcock (1971) says an ancestor of his has a sign saying "Eldorado 1863."

The Eldorado Ditch (called Burnt River Ditch until 1872-1873) was extended headward by increments over a period of over ten years (1863-1874) and eventually carried water from as far as the head of the South Fork of Burnt River west of Unity, more than 125 miles, and 36 air miles to the placers of Malheur. (It's been called the longest placer mining ditch dug in the United States.)

Use of the water carried by the ditch was the subject of many arguments and a few fisticuffs and lawsuits between miners and Burnt River Valley ranchers who needed water from the drainage to irrigate cropland and pastures and water livestock (to feed the miners). The conflicts arose at times when there was not enough water to satisfy both the miners and the ranchers. Duncan and Locey said that wooden flumes that had been erected to carry the ditch water across draws and around rock outcrops were occasionally destroyed by dynamite by irate ranchers. The ditch owners hired gunmen to guard the flumes and walk the ditch.

Duncan (September 4, 1969) says the largest flume was across East Camp Creek. It was 76 feet above the creek bed and 800 feet long. It was built of lumber that must have come from the Koontz mill 40 miles down Burnt River. Ray Duncan (September 8, 1969) also says, "The ditch was never a paying proposition and in order to meet expenses the company used to pay a lot of their men with checks. Those checks were supposed to have been redeemed in cash but most of them never were. Eventually, the company became so involved in debt that it was forced into receivership in 1886. William S. Boswell was appointed receiver. He had built a store in Eldorado in 1864."

Woodcock (1971) said there was a 15-stamp mill at the Black Eagle Mine one-half mile north of Malheur City. The ore there was a soft ore referred to as "pour-free" (probably meaning porphyry). There was another 15-stamp mill at the Red, White and Blue Mine south of Malheur City, which was used to grind hard white quartz ore. Woodcock said when he worked there, the mill treated ore running as high as $400 per ton.

After 1873, the Eldorado Ditch was reduced in size to 24 inches across the bottom and extended on past Amelia to Discovery Gulch, according to Duncan an additional 25 miles (about 12 miles as the crow flies).

Parts of a small propylitized porphyritic felsic pluton, probably altered quartz diorite, near Malheur City in the northern part of Malheur County contains anomalous gold values associated with calcite, chlorite, epidote, and pyrite alteration. Following extensive drilling programs in 1988-1991 company reports by Ican Minerals, Ltd and Billiton Minerals, USA indicate that gold values which range up to 0.078 ounce per ton locally are erratically distributed and grade-tonnage estimates for explored areas are subeconomic. Copper values are under 40 ppm. Size of the mineralized area is said to be about 2,000 by 4,000 feet.

Malheur City

Unity District

Unity District (sometimes called Bullrun District) lies 5 to 9 miles southwest of Unity in Baker County. The gold mines are on the flanks of Mine Ridge and Bullrun Mountain, two north-trending mountain spurs separated by north-flowing Bullrun Creek, a tributary of the South Fork of the Burnt River. Gold and silver production from mines in the district has been more than $203,000 from small lode mines and $36,000 from a dredge placer. The geologic maps of The Rastus Mountain and Bull Run Rock quadrangles (Brooks and Ferns) cover the district. According to those maps, rocks exposed in the area include metamorphosed pre-Jurassic ultramafic rocks and schists, Early and Middle Jurassic clastic sedimentary rocks of the Weatherby Formation, and Jurassic-Cretaceous quartz diorite and diorite that intrudes all the older rocks.

The Ferris Mining Co. operated a dragline dredge with a 3-cubic-yard excavator on Bullrun Creek from October 1940 to July 1941. Output totaled 2,161ounces ($75,635) of gold and 253 ounces of silver from 61,000 yards of gravel. No other records of placer production from the Unity District are known to exist, although it seems likely that some hand placer mining was done in Bull Run Creek before and after the dredging was done.

Quartz mines in the district known to have been productive are the Record Mine, also known as Whited Mine, and the Thomason, Orion, and Bull Run mines. Production from the Record Mine is said to be about $103,000, about $40,000 prior to 1933 and $63,000 between 1933 and 1937. There was some production in the 1980s and 1990s by Kenneth Grabner and Jeff Young. The Thomason Mine produced about $100,000 in the 1980s and 1990s (Art Cheatham, personal communication). Production from the other mines is unknown but, judging from the amount of excavation in evidence, it must have been quite small; the Orion was most active between 1903 and 1917.

The original eight mining claims that made up the Whited Group were located by Alfred Whited and Joe Wahn. The principal ore shoot of the Record Mine is composed of a number of closely spaced parallel stringers of high-grade, gold-bearing quartz in an irregular felsite-porphyry dike along the contact between granodiorite and serpentinite. Most of the ore was oxidized and a high percentage of the gold was free milling . The zone is 5 to 10 feet wide, is nearly vertical, and strikes about N. 60^0 E. The main ore shoot was 100 feet long and 260 feet high. Gold has also been found along with molybdenite and pyrite in thin seams of hornblende associated with the felsite dike. Parks and Swartley (1916) said the mine was active and a 10-stamp mill in operation at the property, which they visited in 1916. A 150-ton amalgamation mill was erected on the property in 1929.

The Thomason Mine produced about $100,000 in gold during the late 1970s and early 1980s. The mine was then owned by Art Cheatham of Ontario, Oregon. He and two partners operated the mine on a small scale during summer and fall months. The ore was in a fracture zone in serpentinized ultramafic rocks. The serpentinite is hydrothermally altered and contains quartz, calcite, talc, pyrite, chalcopyrite, molybdenite, and free gold. The gold commonly coated fracture surfaces in the altered rock. Some very attractive specimens were found. The ore was treated in a one-ton-per-hour gravity mill on the property (Art Cheatham, informant). The ore of the Bull Run mine was found as irregular veins and small lenses, and disseminations in argillite. Ore mineralization at the Orion mine consists of veinlets of pyrite and arsenopyrite in a shear zone in argillite (Lorain, 1938, p.43). Sulfides in the ore were highly oxidized.

Manville Corporation leased the Record mine property in 1984. It is at the northwest end of a block of 200 mining claims located by Manville covering a mineralized zone about 8 miles long and 1 mile wide. Host rocks are sedimentary rocks of the Jurassic Weatherby Formation and granitic rock. Copper and molybdenum mineralization was found locally but apparently not enough to justify pursing development. Manville dropped the claims in the late 1980s.

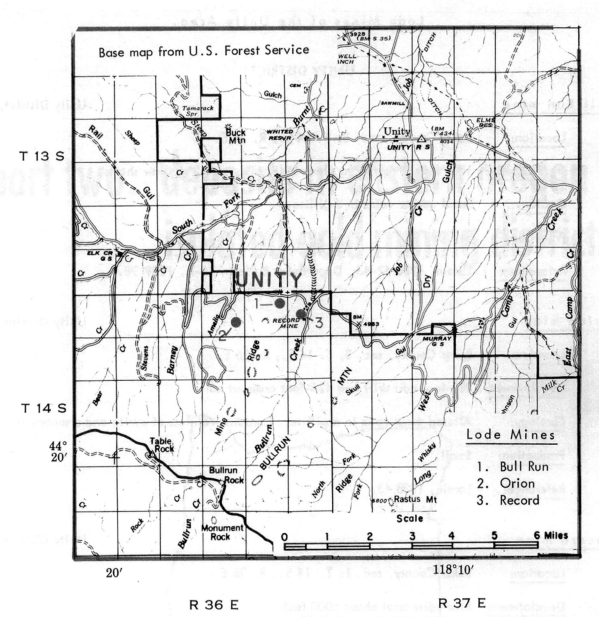

Index map of Unity District

Bibliography

Anderson, A. L., *The Geology and Mineral Resources of the Region about Oro Fino, Idaho:* Idaho Bureau of Mines and Geology Pamphlet 43, 63 p.

Barlow, Jeffrey and Richardson, Christine. (1979) *China Doctor of John Day.* Binford and Mort, Portland, Oregon.

Berkey, Charles P. (undated) "The Sanger Mine." University of Minnesota.

Bishop, Helen Morris. (2003) *In Search of Ancient Oregon: A Geological and Naural History.* Portland, Oregon: Timber Press. 2003.

Bonn, Thomas. (undated) Unpublished notes on Bonanza Placer.

Bowen and Small, publishers. (1898) "Eastern Oregon Gold Fields: Baker, Grant, Harney, Malheur, and Union Counties." *Morning Democrat.*

Brooks, Howard C. (2006) *Preliminary Geologic and Mineral Resources Map of the Mormon Basin 7.5 Minute Quadrangle, Baker and Malheur Counties, Oregon.*

Brooks, Howard C., and others. (1982) *Geology and Gold Deposits of the Granite Quadrangle. Grant County Oregon.* Oregon: Oregon Department of Geology and Mineral Industries Open File Map.

Brooks, Howard C., Ferns, M, L., Coward. R. I., Paul, E. K., and Nunlist. M. (1980) *Geology and gold deposits of the Bourne quadrangle, Baker and Grant Counties.* Oregon: Oregon Department of Geology and Mineral Industries Geological Map Series GMS-19.

Brooks, Howard C. (1979) *Plate Tectonics and the Geologic History of the Blue Mountains.* Oregon Department of Geology and Mineral Industries.

Brooks, H. C. and Vallier, T. L., (1978), *Mesozoic Rocks and Tectonic Evolution of Eastern Oregon and Western Idaho,* in Howell, D.G. and McDougall, K..A. eds., *Mesozoic Paleography of the Western United States: Pacific section, Society of Economic Paleontologists and Mineralogists Pacific Coast Paleogeography 2,* p. 133-146

Brooks, H. C., and Ramp, L. (1968) *Gold and Silver in Oregon.* Oregon Department of Geology and Mineral Industries Bulletin 61, p. 337.

Brosnan, C. J. (1918, 1926) *History of the State of Idaho.* New York, Chicago, Boston: Charles Scribner's, Sons.

Burch, Albert. (1941) "Development of Metal Mining in Oregon," *Oregon Historical Quarterly:* 42.

Bussey, Steven D. and LeAnderson, P. James (1994) *Geology of the Iron Dyke mine and surrounding Hunsaker Creek Formation: in Vallier, T. L. and Brooks, H. C., Geology of the Blue Mountains region of Oregon, Idaho and Washington, Stratigraphy, Physiography, andMineral Resoures of the Blue Mountains Region.* U. S. Geological Survey Bulletin 1439, pp. 151-181

Carrey, John, Cort Conley and Ace Barton. (1979) *Snake River in Hells Canyon.* Cambridge, Idaho: Backeddy Books.

Cheatham, Art. Interviews.

Densley, Lilian Cummings. (1987) *Saints, Sinners, and Snake River Secrets.* Baker, Ore.: The Record-Courier.

Dickinson W. R. and Thayer, T. P. (1984), *Paleogeographic and Paleotectonic Implications of Mesozoic Stratigraphy and Structure in the John Day Inlier of Central Oregon.* In Howell, D. G. and McDougall, K. A. eds. *Mesozoic Paleogeography of the Western United States: Pacific Section of Economic Paleontologists and Mineralogists, Pacific Coast Paleogeography Symposium 2,* p. 147-161.

Dielman, Gary, (ed). (2004) "May Live and Die a Miner: The 1864 Clarksville Diary of James W. Virtue," *Oregon Historical Quarterly,* Spring 2004, 62-95.

Duncan, Ray. "The Big Ditch; a Story of Gold Mining Days in Malheur County, Oregon." Mimeograph copy, 12 pages, no date. Baker City, Oregon : Baker County Public Library.

Duncan, Ray. *"'Big Ditch' 125 Miles Long Was Dug To Water Early Gold Diggings".* Ontario, Oregon: *Argus* Observer, September 4, 8, 15, 1969.

Eastern Oregon's Gold Fields. (1900) *Morning Democrat,* Mining Edition.

Edwards, G. Thomas. "Town Boosterism on Oregon's Mining Frontier: James Vansyckle and Wallula, Columbia Riverport, 1860-1870." History Cooperative. www:historycooperative.org/journals/ohq/106.

Elmer, W.W and Hogg, G. C. Unpublished reports on the Rainbow and Sunday Hill mines in the Mormon Basin District. Oregon Department of Geology and Mineral Industries mine files

Evans, John W. (1990) Powerful Rockey, Eastern Oregon State College at LaGrande Evans, John W. (1990) Powerful Rockey, Eastern Oregon State College at LaGrande

Ferns, Mark L. Howard C. Brooks and Wheeler, 1984, Geology and mineral resoures map of the northwet quarter of the Bates quadrangle, Grant County, Oregon; Oregon Department of Geology and Mineral Industries Geological Map Series GMS-31, scale 1: 24,000.

Ferns, M.L., Brooks, H. C., and Avery D. G., 1983, Geology and gold deposits map of the Greenhorn quadrangle, Grant County, Oregon: Oregon Department of Geology and Mineral Industries, Geological Map Series GMS-28, scale 1: 24,000.

Ferns, M.L., Brooks, H. C., Avery, D. G., and C. D. Blome, 1987, Geology and mineral resourses map of the Elkhorn Peak quadrangle, Baker County, Oregon, Oregon Department of Geology and Mineral Industries, Geological Map Series GMS-41, scale 1: 24,000.

Forsea, Walt. (January 19, 2006) Interview.

Gilluly, J. (1933) *Copper Deposits near Keating.* Oregon: U.S. Geological Survey Bulletin 830-A.

Gilluly, J. (1937) *Geology and Mineral Resources of the Baker Quadrangle.* Oregon: U.S. Geological Survey Bulletin 879.

Gilluly, J., Reed, J. C. and Park, C. F., Jr. *Some mining districts of eastern Oregon.* U.S. Geological Survey Bull. 846-A.

Greg, J. R. Ontario, Oregon: *Argus Observer,* September 21, 1944.

Hailey, John. (1910) *History of Idaho.* Boise, Idaho. Press of Tyms-York.

Hawley, Brooks. (1978) *Gold Dredging in Sumpter Valley.* Baker, Oregon: Baker Printing and Lithography.

Hawley, Brooks. Photo collection notes.

Head, S. Conrade. (1987) *Exploring Northeastern Oregon, Part 1, the Early Gold Era.* La Grande, Oregon: La Grande Publishing Company.

Hiatt, Isaac. (1893) *Thirty-one Years in Baker County.* Baker City, Oregon: Binford and Mort.

History of Baker, Grant, Malheur, and Harney Counties. Western Historical Publishing Co., 1902.

Holland, Carmelita. (1996) *Stories, Legends and Some Oregon History.* Baker City, Oregon: *The Record-Courier,* Printers.

Holiday, Clyde. Telephone interview. August 2, 2004.

Hudson, Wreatha. Conversations.

Idaho City World.. (January 14, 1865) contains an article reporting that Auburn "is fast going to decay."

Lewis, Cecille Lemons. (post 1962) "A short history of Canyon City, discovered June 1862." Unpublished nine-page manuscript, Grant County Oregon Museum.

Lindgren, W. (1901) *The Gold Belt of the Blue Mountains of Eastern Oregon.* U.S. Geological Survey Annual Report, part 2.

Loraine, S. H. *Gold Mining and Milling in Northeastern Oregon.* U. S. Bureau of Mines, Information Circular 7015, May 1938.

Makinson, Clyde. (1980) *History of Sparta, Oregon, Baker County.* Oregon Library.

Mills, Randall V. (1947) *Stern Wheelers Up Columbia.* Palo Alto, California: Pacific Books.

Nielsen, L. E. and D. S. Galbreath. *In the Ruts of the Wagon Wheels.* [S.l.]

Oman, Mary. Unpublished: Flagstaff Mine. U.S. Bureau of Land Management.

Oregon Metal Mines Handbook. (1939, 1941) Oregon Department of Geology and Mineral Industries Bulletin 14-B, Oregon: Department of Geology and Mineral Industries.

Pardee J. T., and Hewett, D. F., (1914), Geology and Mineral Resources of the Sumpter Quadrangle Oregon: Oregon Bureau of Mines and Geology, Mineral Sources of Oregon v. 1, no. 6, p. 7-128

Pardee, J. T. (1941), Preliminary Geologic Map of the Sumpter Quadrangle, Oregon: Oregon Department of Geology and Mineral Industries Quadrangle Map, scale 1:96,000

Parks, H. M. and Swartley, A. M. (1916), *Handbook of the Mining Industry of Oregon:* Oregon Bureau of Mines and Geology, Mineral Resources of Oregon, vol. 2, no. 4, 306 p.

Patera, Allen H. (1994) *Pacific Northwest Mining Camps.* Lake Grove, Oregon: The Depot.

Pine Valley Echo, v. 2. [Richland, OR]

Pine Valley Vignettes. [Richland, OR], 1996.

Prostka, H. J. (1962). *Geology of the Sparta Quadrangle.* Oregon Department of Geology and Mineral Industries mine files, Geologic Map Series GMS-1.

Rand, Helen B. (1981). *Whiskey Gulch.* Baker City Oregon. The Record Courier Printers

Rand, Helen B., (1974) *Gold, Jade, and Elegance.* Baker City Oregon. The Record Courier Printers

Raymond, Rossiter W. *Statistics of Mines and Mining in the States and Territories West of the Rocky Mountains.* United States Commissioner of Mining Statistics, 1870-1877.

Skovlin, Jon M. and Donna McDaniel. (2001) *In pursuit of the McCartys.* Cove, Oregon: Reflections Publishing Co.

Steeves, Laban Richard. (1984) *Chinese Gold Miners in Northeastern Oregon, 1862-1900.* Masters Thesis. Eugene, Oregon: Department of Archaeology, University of Oregon.

Stevens, W. W. "The old Oregon Trail as told by the Trailers." Baker City, Oregon. *The Morning Democrat,* October 1912 to April 1913.

Stewart, Gordon and Patricia. (ca. 1970) *Baker County Sketch Book.* Baker, Oregon*: Baker Democrat Herald* and Baker County Chamber of Commerce.

Stanley G. F. (ed.). (1970) *Charles Wilson's Diary of the Survey of the Forty-ninth Parallel.* Twin Falls County, Idaho: Twin Falls County Library.

Swartley, A. M. (1914) *Ore Deposits of Northeastern Oregon.* Oregon: Oregon Bureau of Mines and Geology, Mineral Resources of Oregon, v. 1 , no. 8.

Tabor, James Waucop. (1988) *Granite and Gold.* Baker, Oregon. *The Reord-Courier,.*

Unpublished reports and notes, Oregon Department of Geology and Mineral Industries, Baker Office, Baker, Oregon.

Vallier, Tracy L. (1974) *Preliminary Report on the Geology of Part of the Snake River Canyon, Oregon.* Department of Geology and Mineral Industries Map GMS-6, scale 1:250,000.

Vallier, Tracy L. (1977) *The Permian and Triassic Seven Devils Group, Western Idaho and Northeastern Oregon.* U.S. Geological Survey, Bulletin 1437, U.S. Government Printing Office, Washington D.C.

Vallier, Tracy L. (1998) *Islands and Rapids: a Geologic Story of Hells Canyon.* Lewiston, Idaho: Confluence Press.

Vhay J, S., (1960), A Preliminary Report on the Copper- Cobalt Deposits in the Quartzburg District: U. S. Geological Survey Open-file Report 60-143. 20 p.

Wagner, N. S. (1967) Unpublished manuscript.

Wallace, Robert. (1976) *The Miners. The Time Life Series, The Old West.* New York: Time, Inc.

Walla Walla Statesman. (October 25, 1862) printed a letter from a correspondent who signed himself "Mack" in Auburn.

Wegars, Pricilla. (1995) *The Ah Hee diggings: final report of archaeological investigations at OR-G-16. The Granite, Oregon "Chinese Walls" site, 1992 through 1994.* Moscow, Idaho: University of Idaho Press.

Wendt, William. Interview.

Woodcock, Ed (as told to Barbara Masterson). (January 6 and 18, 1971) *Early Day Malheur City.* Ontario, Oregon: *Malheur Enterprise.*

Index